FLYING SAILS

OF

MY BOOK HOUSE

EDITED BY

OLIVE BEAUPRÉ MILLER

PUBLISHERS

THE BOOK HOUSE for CHILDREN

LAKE BLUFF, ILL.

LIBRARY OF CONGRESS CATALOG CARD NUMBER 74-155096

PRINTED IN U.S.A.

PREFACE

VOLUME Eight, "Flying Sails," is meant for the period when the interest of boys and girls is turning from fairy tales to real stories of real adventure, full of bold and striking action. To meet the need for true stories at this period, we have in "Flying Sails" actual history tales such as "Young Midshipman David Farragut," and "A Boy on the High Seas." Stories of this type form for boys and girls the introduction to history itself. Even in the fascinating story of the Circus Man, Phineas T. Barnum, and his journey abroad with the famous dwarf, General Tom Thumb, the child meets a number of historical characters. These include Queen Victoria and the Duke of Wellington, who defeated Napoleon at Waterloo and was enormously pleased with Tom Thumb when the little fellow appeared in a miniature of Napoleon's well-known uniform, posing as lost in sorrowful thought over his defeat by Wellington. Thus the child's interest in history is being aroused and he is being prepared to study it.

These latter volumes from eight on through twelve are the volumes which we definitely regard as a school help for the child, since at this age, he is generally reading complete books, usually of doubtful literary merit and adding little to that background of culture which he must have if he is to be a truly educated man or woman. All his life long he finds in art, in music, in literature, in newspapers, even in advertisements and in his business activities, constant reference to the sources of literature. These he must have if he is to get the most out of life and give the most to it.

Therefore, we have not forgotten in "Flying Sails" our literary aims. In this volume of adventure we have included "Gulliver's Travels to Lilliput" by Jonathan Swift, the story of "The Tempest," by Shakespeare, "The Magic Horse" and "The Story of the Talking Bird" from "The Arabian Nights" and the adventures of Maggie Tulliver when she went to live among the gypsies from the novel, "The Mill on the Floss" by George Eliot. Tied with the latter story is "Meg Merrilies," a poem on a gypsy by John Keats, and linked with the tales from "The Arabian Nights" is the poem, "Recollections of the Arabian Nights" by Alfred Tennyson. In addition to these, this volume contains adventure poems by great English poets of a later era, Alfred Noyes and John Masefield, who was also the author of the adventure story, "Mr. Hampden's Shipwreck."

Thus at this period when boys and girls are reading books of none too good quality and are further absorbed by the most exciting and least valuable stories which the radio, television or motion pictures have to offer, "Flying Sails" brings them interesting tales from the literary background they need.

CONTENTS

From *Collected Poems.* Reprinted by permission of Frederick A. Stokes Company.

A Boy on the High Seas

Olive Beaupré Miller

In 1769, when Baltimore was a town of red brick houses and white church steeples with sailing vessels lining its wharves, a young boy named Joshua Barney lived with his mother and father and his thirteen brothers and sisters on a farm not far from the town. Life on the farm was pleasant. There were great estates all around and beautiful plantation houses where people of courtly manners enjoyed life to the full, since their slaves did the work on the farms. But one day the young rascal, Joshua, no more than ten years old, came home from his little log schoolhouse and appeared before his father, his eyes bright and determined and his small chin stubbornly set.

"I'm through with school, sir," he said. "I can write and do arithmetic and I've learned all the master can teach me! I want to go to sea!"

The father was thunderstruck. Up in bleak New England the stony and hostile soil had forced men to take to the sea. Ships from Salem and Newburyport sailed to China and India, and love of a sailor's life was in the very air. But here in the pleasant South, farming was profitable; with slave labor it was easy and men were not as yet much interested in the sea. Joshua, nevertheless, had haunted the waterfront. With yearning eyes, he had watched the beautiful ships glide in, flying like great winged birds over the bounding waves as they made for the Baltimore wharves. The lure of the sea was on him and no one could hold him back. Ten years old and so headstrong! The boy's older brothers feared that some dark night he might secretly do up his clothes in a bundle and run away from home! Worried and half-distracted, his father made the suggestion that he go to work for a merchant, learning to buy and sell cargoes, as the first step in preparing to be the master of a ship! Accordingly, young Joshua was soon in a Baltimore shop, smelling adventure at least, by measuring off linens from Ireland and crimson velvets from Genoa.

But only for three short months was the father allowed to breathe easy. In three months' time the merchant was obliged to close his shop and Joshua turned up at home demanding as he had before: "Father, let me go to sea!"

Mr. Barney now rose up in wrath and exercised his authority. His son should not go to sea. He should go to work for a friend who had a counting house at Alexandria, Virginia. For a year the boy worked like a beaver. Nothing was too much to do if he thought he was getting on toward the goal he held fixed in his mind. Then he went home for Christmas. All the family was there, all his thirteen brothers and sisters. It was a merry occasion with plenty of good things to eat and neighbors riding up on horseback to call out "Merry Christmas!" then drop in to chatter and joke. However, the celebration was scarcely over when Joshua flatly refused to go back to Virginia.

"Father, let me go to sea!" His purpose remained unshaken!

"I'll let you go to work on a Baltimore pilot-boat," the father said in desperation and he added to himself, "That will either put this nonsense out of the boy's head forever or it will toughen his gristle so he can take the hard knocks of a deep-sea sailor's life."

But the boy went to work very eagerly for an old gray-beard of a pilot, and the pilot found the lad so energetic and tireless that he taught him all he knew concerning seamanship. Sometimes their pilot-ship brought in a brig so battered it could scarcely make the wharf, the sailors wounded, limping, and telling most thrilling tales of how they had fought for their lives against free-booting pirates in the blue waters of the Caribbean. At other times they escorted a ship from the Spanish Main, with bags of doubloons and gold ingots taken from the long sunken wreck of some ancient

Spanish galleon. Again, they would sight a signal from a slaver arriving from Guinea with a wretched cargo of blacks jammed in between the decks. Days were full of excitement; but after eight months of this life in the waters close around home, there once again was Joshua appearing before his father and demanding, "Let me go to sea!"

"I'm twelve years old!" he complained. "It's time you stopped coddling me, sir!" So at last his father gave in. One of Joshua's sisters had married a Captain Drysdale who commanded a little brig serving in the Liverpool trade and Mr. Barney consented to apprentice the boy to Drysdale, thus letting him get his start toward realizing his dream.

They sailed in January in the face of a menacing ocean, their little vessel no bigger than a canal boat under sail. Battered by mountainous waves and the bitter winds of winter, half frozen by the cold, they fought their way through storms with a splendid knowledge of seamanship to the docks at Liverpool. There Drysdale sold the vessel and Joshua and he came home.

In a second vessel, the *Sidney*, the two made several voyages; and when the lad reached fourteen, his brother-in-law, finding him always most competent in his work, made him his second mate. He was still apprenticed to Drysdale, his wages belonged to his master, and Drysdale was greedy and surly; but Joshua made no complaints. He was on the deep sea at last.

In December of 1774, Drysdale sailed from Baltimore with a cargo of wheat for Nice, which belonged at that time to Sardinia. Off the capes of Virginia the *Sidney* sprang a leak and had to put back to Norfolk. There repairs were made and part of the cargo discharged; but the captain was in a rage at this little piece of ill luck. He quarreled in the heat of his temper with the first mate of his vessel; the mate picked up his belongings and went ashore in a huff. Unable at such short notice to find another mate, the captain put to sea without one. Then he turned over to Joshua the duties of a first mate. A boy fifteen years old and first mate of a vessel! The ship went along on its way until it reached mid-Atlantic. But there in the vast gray loneliness, Captain Drysdale fell ill and his sickness ended in death. His body was sewed up in canvas, with weights attached to the feet, and in true sailor fashion dropped overboard into the sea.

And now the only officer left on board the *Sidney* was this young lad, Joshua Barney! The crew were men far older and more experienced than he, but for all their great hairy chests and the powerful strength of their muscles, they had no ability to lead, to plan, or to command. All the responsibility had to fall on Joshua.

The easiest thing to do would be to turn back home and report what had happened to the ship-owners, but the boy on thinking things over, determined to finish the voyage and deliver the wheat in Nice to the merchants who had bought it.

Calling the crew together, he announced what he had decided. Astounded, the rough men gaped. A lad little more than a stripling to take command of a vessel!

"The ship is leaking!" they grumbled. "It may founder in bad weather!"

But Joshua assured them that he was perfectly able to use the nautical instruments and keep the boat on her course. He would somehow get them to Nice! Won by the lad's assurance, the sailors agreed to trust him. They worked the pumps with a will to keep the water down and the leaky old boat afloat; but the pumps were not enough. They bailed with wooden pails, snatching only winks of sleep, while Barney urged them on and kept their courage up; but all were greatly relieved when the towering Rock of Gibraltar loomed up on the horizon, guarding the Mediterranean.

Anchor was dropped at Gibraltar just in the nick of time. The *Sidney* could not have floated more than an hour or two longer. Hastily lowering a boat, Barney went off for aid, but when he was half way ashore, he looked back and saw that his men had hoisted the flag upside down. A signal of distress! The boat must be on the verge of plunging to Davy Jones!

Steering hastily alongside two or three other ships, Barney got volunteers to row out to his vessel and relieve the sailors at the pumps. Then he went on his way to seek permission from officials to take his ship into the harbor. Soon she was snug at the dock and Joshua was figuring out how he could get her repaired. Approaching some English merchants by the name of Murray, he made a bargain with them, whereby they agreed to advance the money for repairs in exchange for a bottomry note, a promise to repay the funds when the cargo was sold at Nice. But the price of repairs seemed enormous. Seven hundred pounds sterling! Never had the young apprentice had more than a few small coins to jingle at once in his pocket. Seven hundred pounds sterling! The sum sat heavy on his soul!

In three months' time the *Sidney* was ready for sea again and Barney set out for Nice, taking young Mr. Murray with him; but the ship sprang another leak and Joshua had to land at a port two miles from Nice. He and Murray then went ashore to find the merchants who had bought the wheat. These black moustachioed Sardinians were slippery and over-courteous. They agreed with many fine gestures to pay for the wheat in ten days, that Barney might discharge his debt to the Englishmen in Gibraltar; but when the ten days were up with much of the wheat unloaded Barney went to them again. They received him now with contempt. They had seen a lawyer, they said, and could not be compelled to pay a single ducat! "You are only a boy," they shouted, wagging threatening fingers, "an insolent young apprentice! Your signature of receipt for money we might pay would be altogether worthless! You cannot do business with men!"

Crestfallen, Barney went back to his quarters on the ship. This attempt to cheat him just because he was a boy, was a terrific blow. But he told himself that somehow he would repay that money. His honor was at stake. He was responsible for the debt. Ordering the hatch-covers down, he bade his men see to it that no more grain was unloaded until the bond was paid. The men obeyed with alacrity, hoping that a fight would follow with a chance to take a few punches at the wily Sardinian foe.

In a short time down to the ship came the merchants in high dudgeon! With dramatic gestures, they demanded that Barney proceed with unloading. The wheat belonged to them. Whether

they paid or not, this ridiculous boy must unload the wheat! Saying little or nothing, Joshua glowered at the men until in a rage they rushed off to lay their case before the governor.

The governor agreed with the merchants. He summoned Joshua to him. But even before the awful and august presence of the governor, the boy flatly refused to deliver the wheat without the pay. The governor in a rage then sent him off with some soldiers and cast him into a cell in a filthy Sardinian prison. There Barney took stock of affairs and decided to resort to a trick. He agreed to continue unloading; but when he was thus set free and safe again on his ship, he sent a message back that he would keep all the cargo until the bond was paid. And now he knew well that the governor would send his soldiers against him, so he thought up a little plan to involve that official in trouble. Replacing his usual flags, he hoisted up to the masthead a fluttering British ensign. His colony of Maryland still belonged to England. Let the raging Sardinian Governor, if he blundered into a fight, insult the British flag! There would be the devil to pay! He would have to answer to England!

Impetuously, the governor fell straight into the trap. He sent a strong force of infantry, paying no heed to the ensign and forced Barney off the boat. As Joshua mustered his crew and went off to another English vessel, he gave the Sardinian officer a forceful farewell fling. "I shall leave my colors flying," he said, "that there may be no pretense hereafter of ignorance as to the nation to which this insult has been offered."

Up to this time boyish pride had kept the lad from asking aid or counsel from Mr. Murray. He wanted to chart his own course and get himself out of trouble. But now he called on young Murray. He had one last hope, he said. He would make the dangerous journey over the Alps to Milan and lay his case before the British ambassador to Sardinia. Mr. Murray was staggered by the audacity of the plan; but admiring the pluck of the boy, he agreed at once to go with him.

Together they rode on mule-back, over the steep mountain trails beneath the snow-clad peaks and by deep mountain gorges. At Milan, Barney laid his case before Sir William Lynch, who was the British ambassador. Passing lightly over his own wrongs, he dwelt with artless eloquence on the insult which had so wantonly been offered to the British flag. Sir William was stirred and amused. He sent an immediate protest off to the King of Sardinia. Couriers, that same day, were racing over the Alps, bearing unwelcome dispatches to the high-handed governor at Nice.

It seemed too good to be true. In blithe spirits, Barney and Murray went back over the mountains. And when the city of Nice was still two good leagues distant, what a sight did they see! There, riding post-haste from the city to offer official welcome and escort them back to town, came the governor himself and with him a staff of officers in gold lace, cocked hats, and medals! The governor offered apologies, regrets, and regrets and apologies —with every sort of flowery compliment to the brave, the courageous, most honored, most esteemed Captain Barney!

Thus in this triumphant fashion did Joshua re-enter Nice! An hour after his arrival the knavish Black Moustachios, the wind taken out of their sails, paid him the seven hundred pounds which he turned at once over to Murray.

And now the captains of other ships lying in port at the time hailed the boy as a hero. Dinners were given in his honor. The compliments heaped upon him were enough to turn any lad's head. But Barney took it all modestly with a most unassuming manner.

When his ship had been refitted, he set out for home at last. Intending to complete his voyage just as it had first been planned, he went to load a cargo at Alicante in Spain, but when he reached Alicante, he fell in with more adventures. Charles III of Spain was about to send an expedition against Algerian pirates. These pirates had raided the shipping of all the nations of Europe and were the terror of the Mediterranean. Hoping to exterminate them, Charles was pressing into service every ship coming into Alicante, no matter what flag she flew. Thus he had assembled a magnificent armada of some four hundred vessels. Pennants streaming with color, they rode at anchor on the water while an army of thirty thousand men lay encamped on the shore. So when Barney entered the port, he was ordered to take his place among the waiting ships and go to fight the pirates.

The fleet sailed off to Algiers; but the Spanish leaders were divided by jealousies and hatreds. While they plotted to undo each other, their ships lay idle and useless and a hundred thousand black Moors assembled to prevent a landing. The Spanish commanders then sent ten thousand troops ashore to meet ten times their number. The Moors made a thunderous charge on horseback across a plain. They mowed down their foe like grain, slaughtering them without mercy, and all this horror, Joshua, pacing the deck of his ship, had to stand by and witness, helpless to raise a hand. So complete was the rout that the fleet put to sea and dispersed.

Thus, after months of adventure, Barney reached home at last. His heart beating fast with excitement, he tied up his reports to carry them for inspection to John Smith, the owner of the *Sidney*. No news had reached John Smith of all that had occurred. He knew nothing of Drysdale's death nor of the adventures of the *Sidney*. As the tall, bronzed youth strode quietly into the ship-owner's office, the old man looked up grumpily over the top of his desk. "Who the devil are you?" he demanded.

"I am Joshua Barney, sir, master of your ship, *Sidney*, that has just arrived in port."

"Joshua Barney, eh?" Smith shook an impatient finger. "I remember you! An apprentice bound to Captain Drysdale. How dare you call yourself the master of a ship of mine?"

The boy flung his package of papers on the desk before John Smith. "Read these, sir," he said, "and find out for yourself."

The old man looked through the documents. A long time it took him to read them. But when he had taken in all Joshua had done in his service, he leapt off his stool in a hurry, came over and wrung the boy's hand. "Captain Barney, God bless you!" he cried. "I am proud to find that I have so deserving a young man in my employ."

Captain Barney! Captain Barney! The words fairly made the head of that sixteen year old boy swim. To be called Captain Barney by one who could really bestow that coveted title on him! Captain Barney! Captain Barney! Joshua was a man!*

*Soon after his return Joshua Barney entered the service of the colonies in their war for independence. In 1776 he was made a lieutenant in the new navy of the United States and continued in the service of the navy for many years.

The Tempest*

TOLD FROM THE PLAY BY
WILLIAM SHAKESPEARE

ONCE there lived on a beautiful green island far away in the sea, an old man named Prospero and his lovely daughter Miranda. Miranda could remember no other home but this island, for she was only three years old when she and her father had been shipwrecked on its shores. The two lived together in a cave and Miranda, since her babyhood, had never seen the face of a human being save her father, for there were no other people dwelling on the island.

There was lush green grass. There were fresh springs of crystal water and sweet breezes always blowing. But, there were no people about, for the only other inhabitants were little sprites of the air and an ugly monster named Caliban whose mother, the old witch, Sycorax, had, with her evil spells, once wickedly ruled the place. This old witch had died just before Prospero came; but, before that, she had imprisoned the good little sprites in trees because they would not obey her and there they were shut up, groaning, when Prospero came ashore. Now Prospero was a scholar, he loved books and understood magic, so he set the little sprites free and they ever after obeyed him. A merry crew indeed, were they. Often they danced on the shore, with little feet so light they left no print in the sand. They chased the great waves out to sea and ran before them again as the waves dashed back on the beach. They danced on the green in the moonlight; and the chief of these airy sprites was the dainty Ariel.

*Tchaikovsky's *The Tempest*, based on this story, depicts, in music, a calm sea, then the fury of the storm, the ship-wreck, the beautiful Enchanted Isle, the two lovers, and, at last, the sea, calm again.

Ariel could fly, he could swim, he could dive into flaming fire, he could sleep in a cowslip blossom, he could ride on the curled cloud. But the chief task which Prospero gave him was to keep Caliban in order and make him behave as he should. Prospero had found Caliban long ago in the woods, a misshapen, apelike creature, who could not speak like a human but gabbled like a brute. The good man took Caliban home, let him live in his cave, and taught him how to talk. He also tried with kindness to teach him to act like a man, but Caliban's nature was evil just like that of his mother. He learned nothing good or useful but was always playing wicked tricks and cursing in surly fashion. At last Prospero was obliged to force Caliban to serve him as a master would force a slave. It was Caliban's work to fetch wood, make the fires, and wash the dishes; and, whenever he was lazy and would not perform his tasks, Ariel would come slyly and drive him to his work. Ariel sometimes appeared as a little dancing fire, glimmering hither and thither and leading the monster astray. Sometimes he pinched Caliban or tumbled him down in the mud then, taking the shape of a monkey, he would make grimaces at him; or, in the form of a hedgehog, he lay in Caliban's way pricking the monster's feet. With fear of such mischievous tricks, Ariel managed to drive the savage brute to his tasks.

In general, these sprites of the island were very gentle creatures save when they had to contend with the old witch and her son; but they were powerful, too, and Prospero could, with their help, command the winds and the sea. One day he ordered the sprites to dim the noontide sun, to call forth the roaring winds, to churn up the great green sea until it dashed to the sky, and to let loose the thunder and lightning. In the midst of this terrible tempest, he went down to the shore and showed his daughter a ship—a beautiful, white-winged ship struggling with the wild waters that threatened to swallow it up.

"Oh, my father," cried Miranda, struck to the heart with pity, "on that ship are living creatures like ourselves. If, by your acts, you have raised this tempest, have pity on those poor souls. Had I such power as you, I'd sink the sea beneath the earth, rather than let the waves swallow such a gallant ship!"

"Fear not, daughter," said Prospero, "for I have so ordered it that no smallest harm shall come to anyone on the ship. Only to bring good to you have I stirred up this tempest. My dear one, you do not know who you are nor where you came from! Tell me, can you recall a time before you came to this cave?"

"I can remember a little," Miranda answered her father. "As in a dream, I seem to remember that, when I was a little child, I had four or five women to wait on me, but nothing more whatever can I now recall."

"Four or five women and more you had once to attend you," Prospero cried with spirit, "for, twelve years ago, I was Duke of Milan, and you were a little princess who would have ruled after me. But I had a younger brother by the name of Antonio. I trusted Antonio, daughter; and as I loved to study, I left state affairs to him and spent all my time with my books. But your Uncle Antonio, having thus so much power in his hands, began to dream of making himself Duke of Milan in my stead. He made plans with the King of Naples to get rid of both you and me that he might rule in Milan and make the land subject to Naples. Then he took means to be rid of us."

"Oh, my dear father!" Miranda shuddered at hearing the story of that dread time. "Why, with such plans as those, did my uncle not destroy us?"

"My child," answered Prospero, "they did not dare to destroy us! My people loved me too dearly. Antonio put us on a ship. He took us far out to sea, then forced us into a small boat without either sail or mast. There he left us to perish, to sigh out our sorrow to the winds, who sighed back in pity of us."

"Alack, we two on the sea and I but a babe!" cried Miranda. "What a trouble, dear father, I must have been to you then!"

"Nay, dear heart," said Prospero, "you were a little cherub! Your sweet smiles gave me courage to bear up against misfortune."

"But how did we ever live and come ashore?" asked Miranda.

"By the love of a good friend of mine, one Gonzalo by name." Prospero answered his daughter. "Gonzalo secretly put water, food and clothing and some of the books I so prize into our little boat. Thus we were kept alive until we drifted to this island. Since that time, my child, you have ever been my delight. Teaching you from my books has been my greatest pleasure."

"Would that I might sometime see this good Gonzalo who saved us!" Miranda cried with fervor. "But tell me now, my father, why have you raised this storm?"

"I have raised the storm," cried Prospero, "because, by magic means, I know that my brother Antonio and mine enemy, the King of Naples, are aboard that ship; and, though I shall do them no harm, I want them to be cast ashore here on this island of ours."

Just at that moment Ariel came before his master, unseen by the lovely Miranda, for he was invisible to all except Prospero. Touching Miranda gently with his magic wand, Prospero put her to sleep that she might not hear him talking into thin air, as it were.

"All hail, great master!" cried Ariel. "I have done as you ordered. While the sea roared, I burned as a little flame on the ship—now here, now there on the yards, on the bowsprit, the topmast. The sailors I put to sleep unseen beneath the hatches; but the rest, fever-mad with fear, plunged into the foaming sea. First to leap overboard, his hair on end with terror, was the son of the King of Naples, the young Prince Ferdinand."

"Ah!" cried Prospero. "But you left the young prince safe?"

"Aye," answered Ariel lightly. "He sits lamenting on the seashore, cooling the air with his sighs and holding his head in his hands, for he thinks his father is drowned; while his father, in another place, bemoans his son as dead though he is still searching for him. He wanders with his courtiers in the tangled green wilds of our island. The white-winged ship itself rides safe and sound in the harbor invisible to them all. Not a hair of their heads has been injured. Even their princely garments, though they have been drenched by the sea waves, look fresher than before."

"Well done, my dainty Ariel!" Prospero commended. "Faithfully have you obeyed me. But there is still more for you to do!"

"More to do!" Ariel murmured. "When shall I ever be free?" Dainty, delicate, whimsical, a flighty little sprite of the air, he longed to be free as the wind, free as the wind in the mountains, rushing hither and thither, coming and going at no man's command. "Master," he cried, "remember you have promised me liberty!"

"How now, moody one!" Prospero rebuked him. "Have you forgotten how I freed you when that evil witch Sycorax had imprisoned you in a pine tree and left you to groan in pain and anguish for the free life that you love? Serve me but two days more and then you shall be free."

"What shall I do? I obey!" Ariel felt ashamed of the moment's ingratitude that had made him forget the debt he owed his beloved master.

"Go and bring Ferdinand to me." Prospero ordered gently. "I would have my daughter see this fair young Prince."

So Ariel flitted away to the spot where the young prince sat, sad and lamenting still, on a high bank above the sea. All unseen by the prince, Ariel began to sing:

"Full fathom five thy father lies:
Of his bones are coral made;
Those are pearls that were his eyes:
Nothing of him that doth fade,
But doth suffer a sea-change
Into something rich and strange.
Sea-nymphs hourly ring his knell:
Hark! Now I hear them—Ding-dong, bell."

This strange news of his father roused Ferdinand from his grief. Whence came the voice that sang? From the air, the earth, the sea? Where was this unseen being who knew what fate had befallen the King of Naples, his father? Ferdinand rose and listened. The singing still continued, but the voice drew farther away. Eagerly the young man followed. He could see no living soul, yet ever he heard the voice and it drew him on and on. Thus Ariel led the prince through woods and over meadows to the little stretch of greensward where Prospero and Miranda sat beneath the spreading branches of a beautiful shade tree.

Now Miranda, since she could remember, had never seen a man, except for her own father. She thought all men were grave with long gray beards like her father's and, when this young prince came toward her—his hair shining bright in the sunlight, his lithe figure straight and strong—she was overcome with delight.

"Oh, father," she cried in surprise. "This must surely be some spirit that I see here before me!"

"No, girl," answered her father. "It eats and sleeps and has senses such as we have. This is a young man. He was in the ship that was wrecked and is looking for his companions."

But, if Ferdinand seemed to Miranda so fair and fine a sight, how appealing to Ferdinand was the lovely face of Miranda!

"Beautiful vision!" he cried. "In this place of mysterious music, this island strange of enchantments, are you a maid or are you a goddess?"

"I am but a maid," said Miranda shyly drooping her lashes.

And Prospero, seeing how Ferdinand looked upon Miranda and how at the same time Miranda looked on the face of Ferdinand, knew that they loved each other and that the plan he had made for them was working very well. But he had no mind to let Ferdinand win the maid too easily lest he should prize her too lightly. He secretly made up his mind to set the youth some hard tasks to prove the depth of his love.

"You are a spy," he said sternly, "and you have come to this island to take it away from me, but now you are my prisoner. I will tie you, neck and feet, and you shall drink sea water! Shell-fish, withered roots, and husks of acorns shall be your food."

Henry Purcell (1658-1695), great English composer, wrote beautiful music for *The Tempest.* "Come Unto These Yellow Sands," sung by Ariel to draw Ferdinand to Miranda's presence, is a beautiful song.

"Not I!" cried Ferdinand stoutly, astonished at such a reception yet drawing his sword to fight. "I will resist such treatment." But Prospero waved his magic wand and the prince had no power to move. He stood as though turned to stone.

"Have pity!" Miranda begged, her eyes opened wide toward her father. "This man is no spy! He is noble and brave!"

But Prospero cried to her, "Silence!" And to Ferdinand, "Follow me!" And the prince, through the might of the magic, had no power to disobey. Looking longingly back on Miranda, he followed the old man. "If I may once a day in my prison behold this maid, I shall have liberty enough!" he said as he walked away.

Prospero set him the task of piling up a thousand enormously big logs of wood. Then, smiling into his beard, the old man went into his cave to see what should come to pass.

Very soon Miranda, drawn by her heart's desire, went out and found her lover. With what labor of muscles he toiled! How heavy were the great logs! For pity she could have wept.

"Alas!" she cried with compassion. "Pray do not work so hard. If you'll sit down and rest, I will bear the logs."

"Nay, sweet lady," cried Ferdinand. "I'd rather break my back than have you undergo such a task while I sit by."

"But you look so very weary," Miranda still insisted.

"Weary in your presence I could never be," said the Prince. "Gladly for your sweet sake do I serve as a patient log man."

Looking on, unseen, Prospero smiled to himself. "Things go just as I wish!" he said. "My girl will be the Queen of Naples!"

Meantime, in a distant part of the island, Prospero's false brother, the traitor Antonio, with Prospero's old friend, Gonzalo, other members of the court, and the unhappy King of Naples had worn themselves out with wandering through the woods.

"I beseech you, Sire, be merry!" Gonzalo cried to the King who, in very great grief, was bewailing the loss of his son. "You have cause to rejoice at our escape from the raging sea."

Thus they wandered on until they were almost famished. Suddenly, they heard strains of solemn, mysterious music. Strange, wraithlike shapes appeared bringing along a table spread with a splendid banquet. With gentle gestures the shapes invited the men to eat. They then vanished into the air. "Heavens! What were those things?" cried the old King.

"Their manners are more gentle than those of humankind," Gonzalo answered quietly, for he was secretly thinking how the King had misused Prospero.

Just as the hungry travelers were about to begin eating, there came a wild crash of thunder and brilliant streak of lightning. Then Ariel appeared to them in the form of a hideous harpy, with birdlike body and human head. With a mighty clap of his wings he made the food vanish. Then he shouted in a terrible voice the many crimes of Antonio and the King. "By reason of your wicked deeds against a good man, these misfortunes have befallen you!" he howled. Then he vanished, and the wraithlike shapes came and took away their table, their weird faces mocking the men.

The King of Naples stared as if he had been struck dumb.

"In the name of something holy," cried the good Gonzalo, "why do you stand in that strange stare?"

"'Tis monstrous," shrieked the King. "What monstrous words were these! Methought the willows spoke and told me of my crime. The winds did sing it to me! The thunder roared it likewise! Therefore does my son lie dead. And I should lie beside him!"

"I, too," Antonio cried. "I, too."

"Ah," murmured old Gonzalo, "their guilt, like poison working long after it is taken, now begins to bite their spirits. They are desperate, one and all because of the evil they have done."

But, if these men were sorry for the crimes they had committed, there was another group who were plotting new ill to Prospero.

Caliban had fallen in with a clownish fellow from the ship and a drunken oaf of a butler who had been washed safely to shore.

"What have we here?" cried the clown when he first spied Caliban. "In England I would pay a piece of silver for sight of such a monster!"

"If I could only catch him, I might tame him for a present to the King!" said the butler.

"Do not make fun of me!" cried Caliban.

"But you shall taste my wine. Open your mouth," said the butler.

Never in his life before had Caliban tasted wine.

"Ah," he said as he drank. "This creature must be a god. He bears most heavenly liquor." And he knelt and did homage before him. "Hast thou dropped from Heaven?" he asked.

"Aye, I dropped from the moon," swaggered the drunken butler. "Indeed, I am none other than the man in the moon!"

"I have seen thee in the moon. I do adore thee!" cried Caliban. "I prithee be my god and I will kiss thy foot! I'll show thee every inch of this green fertile island. I'll show thee the best springs of water. I'll pluck thee berries and fish and get thee food enough. A plague on the tyrant I serve! I'll bear him no more sticks. Thee, thee shall I follow, thee, thou wondrous man!"

"I shall laugh myself to death at this puppy-headed monster!" cried the clown in a gale of merriment.

"Let him serve us an' he will," said the butler, "though indeed he be but a moon-calf!"

"I thank my noble lord." Caliban drank more and more out of the butler's bottle. "And I make humble suit to thee to save me from the tyrant who has cheated me of this island. I will lead thee now to the spot where he is sleeping in his cave. Thou mayest easily kill him by putting a nail in his head. Revenge me on this hated man and thou shalt be king of the island. Thou shalt wed his beautiful daughter, and she shall be thy queen."

"Ha, a fair lass!" cried the butler. "Is this daughter then so fair? Methinks I should like a fair lass! Monster, I'll kill this man, this tyrant whom thou hatest!" The butler was now very drunk. "And I will wed his daughter. We will be king and queen! We'll be king and queen of the island!"

Off went the crazy crew, laying their drunken plans. But Ariel overheard them and mischievously fooled them. Lowing like a calf, he led them through thorns and briers, over sticks and stones, to a muddy lake. There he left them, frightened half out of their wits, up to their waists in the mire. Then he went to tell Prospero of this plot against his life.

Prospero by now was convinced that Ferdinand's love was really deep and sincere. He decided to release the young man from his labor of toiling at the woodpile.

"Ferdinand," he said, "if I have severely used you, it was only to try your love. You have nobly stood the test, and I will make rich amends for all the hard tasks I set you, by giving you my daughter."

With deep joy in their hearts, Ferdinand and Miranda warmly embraced each other and, turning to Prospero, they warmly thanked the old man.

Then Prospero said to Ariel, "Go and summon the sprites to assemble here before us and dance in honor of the lovers."

And Ariel said to his master:

"Before you can say 'come' and 'go,'
And breathe twice and say 'so, so,'
Each one tripping on his toe
Will be here with mop and mow."

Off he went, then, to get them, and jolly was the revel. Some of the little sprites appeared as graceful nymphs; others took the form of bronzed, young reapers from the farmlands, and the nymphs sang beautiful songs. Merrily they danced, the

nymphs and the band of reapers, while Ferdinand and Miranda looked on and applauded.

When the dance was over, Ariel said to Prospero, "Antonio, thy brother, and thine old foe, the King of Naples, suffer such pangs of sorrow because of the wrong they did thee that even I, Ariel, pity them and feel sorrow in my heart."

"Then bring them hither," said Prospero. "Since they are truly sorry, my purpose goes not a frown further. If you, my dainty Ariel who are only a spirit, feel pity for their distress, shall not I, who am a human being, have compassion on them?"

"I drink the air before me," Ariel cried with joy, "and return ere your pulse beat twice!" On the wings of the wind, he was off.

Then with sound of his fairy music Ariel led Antonio, the King of Naples, Gonzalo, and all the other courtiers up to the spot where his master stood alone before his cave. But so stupefied were these men with grief and terror of their plight that they did not recognize the man they had so ill-treated.

"Behold, Sir King!" cried Prospero. "Behold the wronged Duke of Milan! It is Prospero who stands here before you!"

All stood stunned for a moment. Could they really believe that Prospero was alive and standing there before them?

Advancing toward the speechless group, Prospero broke their silence by embracing his good and faithful old friend, Gonzalo.

"First, noble friend," he said, "let me embrace thine age whose honor cannot be measured!" And Gonzalo, perceiving at once that this was truly Prospero, returned his embrace with joy.

"If thou art indeed Prospero," cried the King of Naples when he had recovered from his surprise sufficiently to speak, "I do entreat thy pardon and resign to thee thy dukedom."

Prospero bowed his head in forgiveness toward the King, then he turned to his brother, Antonio, who still had no word to say.

"I do forgive thee thy rankest fault," said Prospero to Antonio, "but I require thee to restore my dukedom to me." In a few moments more, they were one and all reconciled to each other and old wrongs had been set right. But, when these matters were settled, thoughts of the King of Naples returned to his lost son.

"Three hours since in ship-wreck I lost my son," he said drooping his head in grief.

But Prospero said to him, "Since you gave me back my dukedom, I will repay your kindness with just as good a thing. I will bring forth a marvel which will content you as much as my returned dukedom does me."

And, opening the door to his cave, he showed the wondering father his son, alive and well, making a pretty picture as he played at chess with Miranda. Ferdinand leaped to his feet and knelt before his father.

"The seas are merciful!" he cried. "I have cursed them without a cause since I see thee, my father, before me!"

"May the blessings of a glad father compass thee!" said the King.

"Oh, wonder!" cried Miranda, breathless at sight of these strangers from a world she had never known. "How beauteous mankind is! O brave new world, that has such people in it!"

"What a fair maid is this!" The King looked at the girl delighting in her beauty and, when he heard that Ferdinand had chosen her for his wife, he gladly gave the couple his blessing and promised that, after him, they should be King and Queen of Naples.

"Now rejoice!" cried old Gonzalo, weeping for gladness to see how men had repented of evil and set their lives straight again. "Here on this isle we deemed ourselves lost, yet here, where we thought ourselves lost, have we truly found ourselves!"

And Prospero added still more to the general joy about him by telling the men that their ship lay safe and sound in the harbor together with the crew. They would all be able on the morrow to take leave of the island and go back home again.

In the midst of this rejoicing, Ariel appeared suddenly, driving before him Caliban and the other two would-be murderers.

"How, now!" cried the King of Naples. "Is not this my drunken butler? Is not this my clownish court jester?"

"So, servant," said Prospero sternly though he silently laughed to himself as he cast a grim eye on the butler. "You would be king of this island! Is that what you thought to be?"

The bulter fell over himself in a fright before his masters.

"A poor king I would make!" he answered stupidly.

"Thrice double ass was I," mumbled Caliban to himself, "to take this drunkard for a god and worship this dull fool!"

Prospero smiled at his servant in amusement and compassion.

"Go into the cave," he said. "Trim it up handsomely, Caliban, and prepare some food for my guests. We will go in and feast in honor of all these happy events whereby we have been made glad!"

And so it was arranged that they should all set out on the very next day for home and Prospero resolved to bury his magic books and never more use the magic arts. Then he called Ariel to him, asked him to see that prosperous winds should attend their homeward journey, and dismissed him from further service.

"My Ariel, chick," said he, "be free and fare thou well."

Ariel shone with joy! How merrily would he live now! In sprightly fashion, he sang his quaint little song of freedom:

"Where the bee sucks, there suck I;
In a cowslip's bell I lie;
There I couch when owls do cry.
On the bat's back I do fly
After summer merrily.
Merrily, merrily shall I live now
Under the blossom that hangs on the bough."

I must go down to the seas again...

SEA-FEVER

By John Masefield

I must go down to the seas again,
to the lonely sea and the sky,
And all I ask is a tall ship
and a star to steer her by,
And the wheel's kick and the wind's song
and the white sail's shaking,
And a grey mist on the sea's face and a grey dawn breaking.

I must go down to the seas again,
for the call of the running tide
Is a wild call and a clear call that may not be denied;
And all I ask is a windy day with the white clouds flying,
And the flung spray and the blown spume,
and the sea-gulls crying.

I must go down to the seas again to the vagrant gypsy life,
To the gull's way and the whale's way
where the wind's like a whetted knife;
And all I ask is a merry yarn from a laughing fellow-rover,
And quiet sleep and a sweet dream when the long trick's over.

AFAR IN THE DESERT

(*South Africa*)

THOMAS PRINGLE

Afar in the desert I love to ride,
With the silent Bush-boy alone by my side.
Away—away from the dwellings of men,
By the wild deer's haunt, by the buffalo's glen;

By valleys remote where the oribi plays,
Where the gnu, the gazelle, and the hartêbeest graze,
And the kudu and eland unhunted recline
By the skirts of gray forest o'erhung with wild vine;

Where the elephant browses at peace in his wood,
And the river-horse gambols unscared in the flood,
And the mighty rhinoceros wallows at will
In the fen where the wild ass is drinking his fill.

Afar in the desert I love to ride,
With the silent Bush-boy alone by my side.
O'er the brown karroo, where the bleating cry
Of the springbok's fawn sounds plaintively;

And the timorous quagga's shrill whistling neigh
Is heard by the fountain at twilight gray;
Where the zebra wantonly tosses his mane,
With wild hoof scouring the desolate plain;

And the fleet-footed ostrich over the waste
Speeds like a horseman who travels in haste,
Hieing away to the home of her rest,
Where she and her mate have scooped their nest,
Far hid from the pitiless plunderer's view
In the pathless depths of the parched karroo.

Afar in the desert I love to ride,
With the silent Bush-boy alone by my side.
Away—away—in the wilderness vast
Where the white man's foot hath never passed,
And the quivered Coranna or Bechuan
Hath rarely crossed with his roving clan.

Gulliver's Travels to Lilliput

By Jonathan Swift

MY FATHER had a small estate in Nottinghamshire. He sent me to Emanuel College, in Cambridge, at fourteen years old, but the charge of maintaining me being too great for a narrow fortune, I was bound apprentice to Mr. James Bates, an eminent surgeon in London. My father now and then sending me small sums of money, I laid them out in learning navigation, and other parts of the mathematics, useful to those who intend to travel, as I always believed it would be sometime or other my fortune to do. When I left Mr. Bates, I went down to my father; where, by the assistance of him and my uncle John, I got a promise of thirty pounds a year to maintain me at Leyden. There I studied physic, knowing it would be useful in long voyages.

Soon after my return from Leyden, I was recommended by my good master, Mr. Bates, to be surgeon to the Swallow, Captain Abraham Pannell, commander, with whom I continued three years and a half, making a voyage or two into the Levant, and some other parts. When I came back, I resolved to settle in London, to which Mr. Bates, my master, encouraged me, and by him I was recommended to several patients. I took part of a small house in the Old Jewry; and being advised to alter my condition, I married Mrs. Mary Burton, with whom I received four-hundred pounds for a portion.

But, my good master Bates dying in two years after and I having few friends, my business began to fail. Having, therefore, consulted with my wife and some of my acquaintance, I determined to go again to sea and made several voyages to the East and West Indies. My hours of leisure I spent in reading the best authors and, when I was ashore, in observing the manners and disposition of the people, as well as learning their language, wherein I had a great facility by the strength of my memory.

The last of these voyages not proving very fortunate, I grew weary of the sea, and intended to stay at home with my wife and family, hoping to get business among the sailors; but it would not turn to account. After three-years' expectation that things would mend, I accepted an advantageous offer from Captain William Pritchard, master of the Antelope, who was making a voyage to the South Sea. We set sail from Bristol, May 4th, 1699. In our

passage from thence to the East Indies, we were driven by a violent storm to the northwest of Van Diemen's Land.

Twelve of our crew were dead by immoderate labor and ill food, the rest were in a very weak condition. On the fifth of November, which was the beginning of summer in those parts, the weather being very hazy, the seamen spied a rock within half a cable's length of the ship; but the wind was so strong that we were driven directly upon it and immediately split. Six of the crew, of whom I was one, having let down the boat into the sea, made a shift to get clear of the ship and the rock.

We rowed by my computation, about three leagues, till we were able to work no longer, being already spent with labor while we were in the ship. We therefore trusted ourselves to the mercy of the waves, and, in about half an hour, the boat was overset by a sudden flurry from the North.

What became of my companions in the boat, as well as of those who escaped on the rock or were left in the vessel, I cannot tell but conclude they were all lost.

For my own part, I swam as fortune directed me and was pushed forward by wind and tide. I often let my legs drop and could feel no bottom, but, when I was almost gone and able to struggle no longer, I found myself within my depth; and, by this time, the storm was much abated. The declevity was so small that I walked near a mile before I got to the shore, which I conjectured was about eight o'clock in the evening. I then advanced forward near half a mile, but could not discover any sign of houses or inhabitants; at least, I was in so weak a condition that I did not observe them.

I was extremely tired and with that and the heat of the weather and about half a pint of brandy that I drank as I left the ship, I found myself much inclined to sleep. I lay down on the grass, which was very short and soft, where I slept sounder than ever I remembered to have done in my life, and, as I reckoned, about nine hours; for, when I awaked, it was just daylight.

I attempted to rise, but was not able to stir for, as I happened to lie on my back, I found my arms and legs were strongly fastened on each side to the ground; and my hair, which was long and thick, tied down in the same manner. I likewise felt several slender ligatures across my body, from my armpits to my thighs. I could only look upward, the sun began to grow hot, and the light offended my eyes. I heard a confused noise about me, but, in the posture I lay, could see nothing except the sky.

In a little time I felt something alive moving on my left leg, which, advancing gently forward over my breast, came almost up to my chin; when bending my eyes downward as much as I could, I perceived it to be a human creature not six-inches high, with a bow and arrow in his hands and a quiver at his back. In the meantime, I felt at least forty more of the same kind, as I conjectured, following the first.

I was in the utmost astonishment, and roared so loud, that they all ran back in a fright; and some of them, as I was afterward told, were hurt with the falls they got by leaping from my sides upon the ground.

However, they soon returned and one of them, who ventured so far as to get a full sight of my face, lifting up his hands and eyes by way of admiration, cried out in a shrill but distinct voice, "*Hekinah degul!*" The others repeated the same words several times, but I then knew not what they meant.

I lay all this while, as the reader may believe, in great uneasiness. At length, struggling to get loose, I had the fortune to break the strings and wrench out the pegs that fastened my left arm to the ground; for, by lifting it up to my face, I discovered the methods they had taken to bind me. And, at the same time, with a violent pull which gave me excessive pain, I a little loosened the strings that tied down my hair on the left side, so that I was just able to turn my head about two inches.

But the creatures ran off a second time, before I could seize

them; whereupon there was a great shout in a very shrill accent, and, after it ceased, I heard one of them cry aloud: "*Tolgo phonac!*"

In an instant I felt above an hundred arrows discharged on my left hand, which pricked me like so many needles; and, besides, they shot another flight into the air, as we do bombs in Europe, whereof many, I suppose, fell on my body (though I felt them not) and some on my face, which I immediately covered with my left hand. When this shower of arrows was over, I fell a-groaning with grief and pain, and then striving again to get loose, they discharged another volley larger than the first, and some of them attempted with spears to stick me in the sides; but, by good luck, I had on me a buff jerkin, which they could not pierce.

I thought it the most prudent method to lie still, and my design was to continue so till night, when my left hand being already loose, I could easily free myself. As for the inhabitants, I had reason to believe I might be a match for the greatest army they could bring against me, if they were all of the same size with him that I saw. But fortune disposed otherways of me. When the people observed I was quiet, they discharged no more arrows; but, by the noise I heard, I knew their numbers increased and about four yards from me, over against my right ear, I heard a knocking for above an hour like that of people at work; when turning my head that way, as well as the pegs and strings would permit me, I saw a stage erected, about a foot and a half from the ground, capable of holding four of the inhabitants, with two or three ladders to mount it. From whence one of them, who seemed to be a person of quality, made me a long speech, whereof I understood not one syllable.

But I should have mentioned that before the principal person began his oration, he cried out three times, "*Langro dehul san!*" (These words and the former were afterwards repeated and explained to me.) Whereupon immediately about fifty of the inhabitants came and cut the strings that fastened the left side of my head, which gave me the liberty of turning it to the right and of observing the person and gesture of him that was to speak. He appeared to be of a middle age, and taller than any of the other three who attended him, whereof one was a page that held up his train, and seemed to be somewhat longer than my middle finger;

the other two stood one on each side to support him. He acted every part of an orator, and I could observe many periods of threatening and others of promises, pity, and kindness. I answered in a few words, but in the most submissive manner, lifting up my left hand and both my eyes to the sun, as calling him for a witness; and, being almost famished with hunger, having not eaten a morsel for some hours before I left the ship, I found the demands of nature so strong upon me that I could not forbear showing my impatience, perhaps against the strict rules of decency, by putting my finger frequently to my mouth to signify that I wanted food.

The Hurgo (for so they called a great lord, as I afterward learned) understood me very well. He descended from the stage and commanded that several ladders should be applied to my sides, on which above an hundred of the inhabitants mounted and walked toward my mouth, laden with baskets full of meat which had been provided and sent thither by the king's orders upon the first intelligence he received of me. I observed there was the flesh of several animals, but could not distinguish them by the taste. There were shoulders, legs, and loins, shaped like those of a mutton and very well-dressed, but smaller than the wings of a lark. I ate them by two or three at a mouthful and took three loaves at a time, about the bigness of musket bullets. They supplied me as they could, showing a thousand marks of wonder and astonishment at my bulk and appetite. I then made another sign that I wanted drink. They found by my eating that a small quantity would not suffice me and, being a most ingenious people, they flung up with great dexterity, one of their largest hogsheads, then rolled it toward my hand and beat out the top.

I drank it off at a draught, for it did not hold half a pint, and tasted like a small wine of Burgundy, but much more delicious. They brought me a second hogshead, which I drank in the same manner, and made signs for more; but they had none to give me.

When I had performed these wonders, they shouted for joy

and danced upon my breast, repeating several times as they did at first, "*Hekinah degul.*" I confess I was often tempted, while they were passing backward and forward on my body, to seize forty or fifty of the first that came in my reach, and dash them against the ground. But the remembrance of what I had felt and the promise of honour I made them, for so I interpreted my submissive behaviour, soon drove out these imaginations. Besides, I now considered myself bound by the laws of hospitality to a people who had treated me with so much expense and magnificence.

After some time, when they observed that I made no more demands for meat, there appeared before me a person of high rank from his Imperial Majesty. His Excellency, having mounted on the small of my right leg, advanced forward up to my face, with about a dozen of his retinue. And producing his credentials which he applied close to my eyes, spoke about ten minutes without any signs of anger often pointing forward, which as I afterward found, was toward the capital city—about half a mile distant, whither, it was agreed by his Majesty that I must be conveyed.

I made a sign with my hand to signify that I desired my liberty. He shook his head by way of disapprobation and held his hand in a posture to show that I must be carried as a prisoner. However, he made other signs to let me understand that I should have meat and drink enough, and very good treatment. Whereupon I once more thought of attempting to break my bonds; but again, when I felt the smart of their arrows upon my face and hands, which were all in blisters, and observed likewise that the number of my enemies increased, I gave token to let them know that they might do with me as they pleased.

Upon this, the Hurgo and his train withdrew with much civility. Soon after, I heard a general shout, with frequent repetitions of the words, "*Peplom selan,*" and I felt great numbers of people on my left side, relaxing the cords to such a degree that I was able to turn upon my right. But before this, they had daubed my face and hands with a sort of ointment very pleasant to the smell, which removed all the smart of their arrows.

These circumstances, added to the refreshment I had received by their victuals and drink which were very nourishing, disposed me to sleep. I slept about eight hours, as I was afterward assured; and it was no wonder, for the physicians, by the Emperor's order, had mingled a sleepy potion in the hogsheads of wine.

It seems that, upon the first moment I was discovered sleeping on the ground after my landing, the Emperor had early notice of it by an express and determined in council that I should be tied in the manner I have related (which was done in the night while I slept), that plenty of meat and drink should be sent to me, and a machine prepared to carry me to the capital city.

These people are most excellent mathematicians, and arrived to a great perfection in mechanics, by the encouragement of the Emperor, who is a renowned patron of learning. This prince hath several machines fixed on wheels, for the carriage of trees, and other great weights. He often builds his largest men-of-war, whereof some are nine feet long, in the woods where the timber grows, and has them carried on these engines three- or four-hundred yards to the sea.

Five-hundred carpenters and engineers were immediately set at work to prepare the greatest engine they had. It was a frame of wood raised three inches from the ground, about seven feet long, and four wide, moving upon twenty-two wheels. The shout I heard was upon the arrival of this engine, which, it seems, set out in four hours after my landing.

It was brought parallel to me as I lay. But the principal difficulty was to raise and place me in this vehicle. Eighty poles, each of one foot high, were erected for this purpose, and very strong cords were fastened by hooks to many bandages which the workmen had girt round my neck, my hands, my body, and my legs. Nine-hundred of the strongest men were employed to draw up these cords by many pulleys fastened on the poles; and thus, in less than three hours, I was raised and flung into the engine, and there tied fast. All this I was told, for, while the whole operation was performing, I lay in a profound sleep. Fifteen-hundred of the Emperor's largest horses, each about four inches and a half high, were employed to draw me toward the metropolis.

About four hours after we began our journey, I awaked by a ridiculous accident, for the carriage being stopped awhile to adjust something, two or three of the natives had the curiosity to see how I looked when I was asleep. They climbed up into the engine and, advancing softly to my face, one of them, an officer in the Guards, put the sharp end of his half-pike a good way up into my left nostril which tickled my nose like a straw and made me sneeze violently whereupon they stole off unperceived. It was three weeks before I knew the cause of my awaking so suddenly.

We made a long march that day and rested at night with five-hundred guards on each side of me—half with torches and half with bows and arrows—ready to shoot me, if I should offer to stir. The next morning, at sunrise, we continued our march and arrived within two-hundred yards of the city gates about noon. The Emperor and all his court came out to meet us, but his officers would by no means suffer his Majesty to endanger his person by mounting on my body.

At the place where the carriage stopped, there stood an ancient temple esteemed to be the largest in the whole kingdom, which, having been polluted some years before by an unnatural murder, was, according to the zeal of those people, looked on as profane and therefore had been applied to common use, and all the ornaments and furniture carried away. In this edifice, it was determined I should lodge. The great gate fronting to the North was about four feet high and almost two feet wide, through which I could easily creep. On each side of the gate was a small window, not above six inches from the ground. Into that on the left side, the King's smith conveyed fourscore-and-eleven chains, like those that hang to a lady's watch in Europe. These were locked to my left leg, with six-and-thirty padlocks. Over against this temple, on t'other side of the great highway, was a turret at least five feet high. Here the Emperor ascended, with many principal lords of his court, to have an opportunity of viewing me.

It was reckoned that above an hundred-thousand inhabitants came out of the town upon the same errand; and, in spite of my guards, I believe there could not be fewer than ten-thousand, at several times, who mounted my body by the help of ladders. But a proclamation was soon issued to forbid it upon pain of death. When the workmen found it was impossible for me to break loose, they cut all the strings that bound me, whereupon I rose up with as melancholy a disposition as ever I had in my life. But the astonishment of the people, at seeing me rise and walk, is not to be expressed. The chains that held my left leg were about two yards long and gave me not only the liberty of walking backward and forward in a semicircle, but, being fixed within four inches of the gate, allowed me to creep out of it.

When I found myself on my feet, I looked about me and must confess I never beheld a more entertaining prospect. The country round appeared like a continual garden, and the enclosed fields, which were generally forty feet square, resembled so many beds of flowers. These fields were intermingled with woods of half a stang, and the tallest trees, as I could judge, appeared to be seven feet high. I viewed the town on my left hand, which looked like the painted scene of a city in a theatre.

The Emperor was already descended from the tower and, advancing on horseback toward me, which had like to have cost him dear for the beast, wholly unused to such a sight which appeared as if a mountain moved before him, reared up on his hind feet, but that Prince who is an excellent horseman kept his seat, till his attendants ran in and held the bridle, while his Majesty had time to dismount. When he alighted, he surveyed me round with great admiration, but kept without the length of my chain. He ordered his cooks and butlers, to give me victuals and drink which were pushed forward in a sort of vehicle on wheels. I took these vehicles and soon emptied them all. Twenty of them were filled with meat, and ten with liquor.

The Empress and young Princes of the blood, attended by many ladies, sat at some distance in their chairs; but, upon the accident that happened to the Emperor's horse, they alighted and came near his person, which I am now going to describe. He is taller by almost the breadth of my nail than any of his court. His features are strong and masculine, his complexion olive, his countenance erect, his body and limbs well-proportioned, his motions graceful, and his deportment majestic.

He was then past his prime, being twenty-eight years and three-quarters old, of which he had reigned about seven, in great felicity and generally victorious. For the better convenience of beholding him, I lay on my side so that my face was parallel to his, and he stood but three yards off. However, I had him since many times in my hand and, therefore, cannot be deceived in the description. His dress was very plain and simple, and the fashion of it, between the Asiatic and the European; but he had on his head a light helmet of gold, adorned with jewels, and a plume on the crest. He held his sword drawn in his hand to defend himself, if I should happen to break loose. It was almost three inches long, the hilt and scabbard were gold enriched with diamonds. His voice was shrill, but very clear and articulate.

The ladies and courtiers were all most magnificently clad, so that the spot they stood upon seemed to resemble a petticoat spread on the ground, embroidered with figures of gold and silver. His Imperial Majesty spoke often to me and I returned answers, but neither of us could understand a syllable. There were several of his priests and lawyers present who were commanded to address themselves to me, and I spoke to them in as many languages as I had the least smattering of, but all to no purpose.

After about two hours the court retired, and I was left with a strong guard, to prevent the impertinence of the rabble, who were impatient to crowd about me as near as they durst, and some of them had the impudence to shoot their arrows at me as I sat on the ground by the door of my house, whereof one very narrowly missed my left eye. But the colonel ordered six of the ringleaders to be seized, and thought no punishment so proper as to deliver them bound into my hands, which some of his soldiers accordingly did, pushing them forward with the butt ends of their pikes into my reach. I took them all in my right hand, put five of them into my coat pocket, and as to the sixth, I made a countenance as if I would eat him alive. The poor man squalled terribly, and the colonel and his officers were in much pain, especially when they saw me take out my penknife. But I soon put them out of fear, for, looking mildly and immediately cutting the strings he was bound with, I set him gently on the ground, and away he ran. I treated the rest in the same manner, taking them one by one out of my pocket, and I observed both the soldiers and people were obliged at this mark of my clemency, which was represented very much to my advantage at court.

Toward night I got with some difficulty into my house, where I lay on the ground and continued to do so about a fortnight, during which time, the Emperor gave orders to have a bed prepared for me. Six-hundred beds of the common measure were brought in carriages and worked up in my house. An hundred-and-fifty of their beds, sewn together, made up the breadth and length; and these were four double, which, however, kept me but very indifferently from the hardness of the floor.

As the news of my arrival spread through the kingdom, it brought prodigious numbers of rich, idle, and curious people to see me, so that the villages were almost emptied, and great neglect of tillage and household affairs must have ensued, if his Imperial Majesty had not provided, by several proclamations and orders of State, against this inconveniency. He directed that those who had already beheld me should return home and not presume to come within fifty yards of my house, without license from court.

In the meantime, the Emperor had frequent councils to debate what course should be taken with me; and I was afterward assured by a particular friend, a person of great quality, that the court was under many difficulties concerning me. They apprehended my breaking loose, that my diet would be very expensive and might cause a famine. Sometimes they determined to starve me, or shoot me with poisoned arrows, but again they considered that the stench of so large a carcass might produce a plague in the metropolis, and probably spread through the whole kingdom.

In the midst of these consultations, several officers of the army went to the great council chamber and gave an account of my behaviour to the six criminals above-mentioned. This made so favourable an impression in the breast of his Majesty and the whole board in my behalf, that an Imperial Commission was issued out, obliging all the villages, nine-hundred yards round the city, to deliver in every morning six beeves, forty sheep, and other victuals for my sustenance, together with a proportionable quantity of bread and wine and other liquors; for the due payment of which, his Majesty gave assignments upon his treasury.

An establishment was also made of six-hundred persons to be my domestics, who had tents built for them on each side of my door. It was likewise ordered that three-hundred tailors should make me a suit of clothes after the fashion of the country, that six of his Majesty's greatest scholars should be employed to instruct me in their language, and, lastly, that the Emperor's horses and those of the nobility and troops of guards should be frequently exercised in my sight, to accustom themselves to me.

All these orders were duly put in execution, and, in about three weeks, I made a great progress in learning their language, during which time, the Emperor frequently honoured me with his visits and was pleased to assist my masters in teaching me. We began already to converse together in some sort, and the first words I learned were to express my desire that he would please to give me my liberty, which I every day repeated on my knees. His answer, as I could apprehend it, was that this must be a work of time, and that first I must "*Lumos kelmin peffo defmar lon Emposo*"; that is, swear a peace with him and his kingdom. However, that I should be used with all kindness; and he advised me to acquire, by my patience and discreet behaviour, the good opinion of himself and his subjects.

He desired I would not take it ill, if he gave orders to certain proper officers to search me, for probably I might carry about me several weapons, which must needs be dangerous things if they answered the bulk of so prodigious a person. I said his Majesty should be satisfied for I was ready to strip myself and turn up my pockets before him. This I delivered, part in words, and part in signs. He replied, that by the laws of the kingdom, I must be searched by two of his officers; that he had so good an opinion of my generosity and justice as to trust their persons in my hands; that whatever they took from me, should be returned when I left the country, or paid for at the rate which I would set upon them. I took up the officers in my hands, put them first into my coat pockets, and then into every other pocket about me except my two fobs, and another secret pocket I had no mind should be searched, wherein I had some little necessaries that were of no consequence to any but myself. In one of my fobs there was a silver watch, and in the other a small quantity of gold in a purse. These gentlemen, having pen, ink, and paper about them made an exact inventory of everything they saw; and, when they had done, desired I would set them down, that they might deliver it to the Emperor. This inventory I afterward translated into English, and is word for word as follows:

"In the right coat pocket of the 'Great Man-Mountain,' after the strictest search, we found only one great piece of coarse cloth large enough to be a foot-cloth for your Majesty's chief room of state. In the left pocket, we saw a huge silver chest with a cover of the same metal, which we, the searchers, were not able to lift. We desired it should be opened, and one of us stepping into it, found himself up to the mid-leg in a sort of dust, some part whereof flying up to our faces set us both a sneezing for several times.

In his right waistcoat pocket, we found a prodigious bundle of white, thin substances, tied with a strong cable, and marked with black figures which we humbly conceive to be writings—every letter almost half as large as the palm of our hand.

"In the left, there was a sort of engine, from the back of which were extended twenty long poles, resembling the palisadoes before your Majesty's court; wherewith we conjecture the Man-Mountain combs his head.

"In the large pocket on the right side of his middle cover (so I translate the word *Ranfu-Lo*, by which they meant my breeches), we saw a hollow pillar of iron about the length of a man, fastened to a strong piece of timber. In the left pocket, another engine of the same kind. In the smaller pocket on the right side, were several round, flat pieces of white-and-red metal of different bulk; some of the white, which seemed to be silver, were so large and heavy, that my comrade and I could hardly lift them.

"In the left pocket, were two black pillars, irregularly shaped. We could not, without difficulty, reach the top of them, as we stood at the bottom of his pocket. Within each of these was enclosed a prodigious plate of steel; which, by our orders, we obliged him to show us, because we apprehended they might be dangerous engines. He took them out of their cases and told us that, in his own country, his practice was to shave his beard with one of these and to cut his meat with the other.

"There were two pockets which we could not enter. These he called his fobs. They were two large slits cut into the top of his middle cover, but squeezed close by the pressure of his belly.

Out of the right fob hung a great silver chain, with a wonderful kind of engine at the bottom. We directed him to draw out whatever was fastened to that chain; which appeared to be a globe, half-silver and half of some transparent metal, for on the transparent side, we saw certain strange figures, circularly drawn. He put this engine to our ears, which made an incessant noise like that of a water mill. And we conjecture, it is either some unknown animal or the god that he worships; but we are more inclined to the latter opinion, because he assured us that he seldom did anything without consulting it. He called it his oracle and said it pointed out the time for every action of his life.

"From the left fob he took out a net almost large enough for a fisherman, but contrived to open and shut like a purse and served him for the same use. We found therein several pieces of yellow metal, which, if they be real gold, must be of immense value.

"Having thus, in obedience to your Majesty's commands, diligently searched all his pockets, we observed a girdle about his waist from which, on the left side, hung a sword of the length of five men and on the right, a bag or pouch divided into two cells, each cell capable of holding three of your Majesty's subjects. In one of these cells were several globes, or balls of a most ponderous metal about the bigness of our heads, and required a strong hand to lift them. The other cell contained a heap of certain black grains, but of no great bulk or weight for we could hold above fifty of them in the palms of our hands.

"This is an exact inventory of what we found about the body of the Man-Mountain, who used us with civility, and due respect to your Majesty's commission. Signed and sealed, on the fourth day of the eighty-ninth moon of your Majesty's auspicious reign."

Clefrin Frelock, Marsi Frelock.

When this inventory was read over to the Emperor, he directed me, although in very gentle terms, to deliver up the several particulars. In the meantime, he ordered three-thousand of his choicest troops to surround me at a distance with their bows and arrows just ready to discharge. He then desired me to draw my scimitar. I did so and, immediately, all the troops gave a shout between terror and surprise for the sun shone clear and the reflection dazzled their eyes, as I waved the scimitar to and fro in my hand. His Majesty was less daunted than I could expect. He ordered me to return it into the scabbard and cast it on the ground as gently as I could, about six feet from the end of my chain.

The next thing he demanded was one of the hollow iron pillars, by which he meant my pocket pistols. I drew it out and, at his desire, as well as I could, expressed to him the use of it; and charging it only with powder, I first cautioned the Emperor not to be afraid, and then I let it off into the air. The astonishment here was much greater than at the sight of my scimitar. Hundreds fell down, as if they had been struck dead; and even the Emperor, although he stood his ground, could not recover himself in sometime. I delivered up both my pistols in the same manner as I had done my scimitar, and then my pouch of powder and bullets, begging him, that the former might be kept from the fire, for it would kindle with the smallest spark and blow up his imperial palace into the air.

I likewise delivered up my watch, which the Emperor was very curious to see, and commanded two of his tallest yeomen of the guards to bear it on a pole upon their shoulders, as draymen in England do a barrel of ale. He was amazed at the continuous noise it made and the motion of the minute-hand, and asked the opinions of his learned men about him. I then gave up my silver and copper money; my purse with nine large pieces of gold, and some smaller ones; my knife and razor; my comb and silver snuffbox; my handkerchief and journal-book. My scimitar, pistols, and pouch were conveyed in carriages to his Majesty's stores, but the rest of my goods were returned me.

I had, as I before observed, one private pocket which escaped their search, wherein there was a pair of spectacles, a pocket perspective, and several other conveniences which I apprehended might be lost or spoiled if I ventured them out of my possession.

My gentleness and good behaviour had gained so far on the Emperor and his court and, indeed, upon the army and people in general that I began to conceive hopes of getting my liberty in a short time. The natives came, by degrees, to be less apprehensive of any danger from me.

I would sometimes lie down and let five or six of them dance on my hand; and, at last, the boys and girls would venture to come and play at hide-and-seek in my hair.

The Emperor had a mind, one day, to entertain me with country shows, wherein they exceed all nations I have known, both for dexterity and magnificence. I was diverted with none so much as that of the rope-dancers performed upon a slender white thread, extended about two feet and twelve inches from the ground.

The horses of the army and those of the royal stables, having been daily led before me, were no longer shy but would come up to my very feet without starting. The riders would leap them over my hand as I held it on the ground; and one of the Emperor's huntsmen, upon a large courser, took my foot, shoe and all. It was, indeed, a prodigious leap.

I had the good fortune to divert the Emperor, one day, after a very extraordinary manner. I desired he would order several sticks of two feet high and the thickness of an ordinary cane, to be brought me, whereupon his Majesty commended the master of his woods to give directions accordingly, and the next morning six woodmen arrived with as many carriages drawn by eight horses to each. I took nine of these sticks and, fixing them firmly in the ground in a quadrangular figure, two feet and a half square, I took four other sticks and tied them parallel at each corner about two feet from the ground. I fastened my handkerchief to nine sticks that stood erect, and extended it on all sides till it was as tight as the top of a drum, and the four parallel sticks, rising about five inches higher than the handkerchief, served as ledges on each side. When I had finished my work, I desired the Emperor to let a troop of his best horses, twenty-four in number, come and exercise upon this plain.

His Majesty approved of the proposal, and I took them up one by one in my hands, ready mounted and armed, with the proper officers to exercise them. As soon as they got in order, they divided into two parties, performed mock skirmishes, discharged blunt arrows, drew their swords, fled and pursued, attacked and retired, and, in short, discovered the best military discipline I ever beheld. The parallel sticks secured them and their horses from falling over the stage; and the Emperor was so much delighted, that he once was pleased to be lifted up and give the word of command; and, with great difficulty, persuaded even the Empress herself to let me hold her in her chair within two yards of the

stage from whence she was able to take a full view of the whole performance. It was by good fortune that no ill accident happened in these entertainments, only once a fiery horse, that belonged to one of the captains, pawing with his hoof, struck a hole in my handkerchief and, his foot slipping, he overthrew his rider and himself; but I immediately relieved them both, and covering the hole with one hand, I set down the troop with the other in the same manner as I took them up.

As I was entertaining the court with these kind of feats, there arrived an express to inform his Majesty that some of his subjects, riding near the place where I was first taken up, had seen a great black substance lying on the ground, very oddly shaped, extending its edges round as wide as his Majesty's bedchamber and rising up in the middle as high as a man.

It was no living creature, as they at first apprehended, for it lay on the grass without motion. Some of them had walked round it several times. By mounting upon each other's shoulders, they got to the top, which was flat and even, and, stamping upon it, they found it was hollow within. They humbly conceived it might be something belonging to the Man-Mountain; and, if his Majesty pleased, they would undertake to bring it with only five horses. I presently knew what they meant and was glad at heart to receive this intelligence.

It seems upon my first reaching the shore after our shipwreck, I was in such confusion, that, before I came to the place where I went to sleep, my hat, which I had fastened with a string to my head while I was rowing and had stuck on all the time I was swimming, fell off after I came to land. I entreated his Imperial Majesty to give orders it might be brought to me as soon as possible, describing to him the use and the nature of it; and the next day the waggoners arrived with it, but not in a very good condition. They had bored two holes in the brim within an inch and a half of the edge and fastened two hooks in the holes; these hooks were tied by a long cord to the harness, and thus my hat was dragged along for above half an English mile.

Two days after this adventure, the Emperor took a fancy of diverting himself in a very singular manner. He desired I would stand like a colossus with my legs as far asunder as I conveniently could, he then commanded his general to draw up the troops in close order and march them under me; the foot by twenty-four in a breast and the horse by sixteen, with drums beating, colours flying, and pikes advanced.

I had sent so many memorials and petitions for my liberty, that his Majesty at length mentioned the matter first in the cabinet, and then in a full council where it was opposed by none, except Skyresh Bolgolam, the Admiral of the Realm who was pleased, without any provocation, to be my mortal enemy. However, he was at length persuaded to comply, but prevailed that the conditions upon which I should be set free, should be drawn up by himself. These articles were brought to me by Skyresh Bolgolam in person, attended by several persons of distinction. After they were read, I was demanded to swear to the performance of them in the method described by their laws, which was to hold my right foot in my left hand and to place the middle finger of my right hand on the crown of my head, and my thumb on the tip of my right ear. I have made a translation of the whole instrument, as near as I was able, which I here offer to the public.

"GOLBASTO MOMAREN EVLAME GURDILO SHEFIN MULLY ULLY GUE, most mighty Emperor of Lilliput, delight and terror of the universe, whose dominions extend five-thousand blustrugs (about twelve miles in circumference), to the extremities of the globe; monarch of all monarchs, taller than the sons of men; whose feet press down to the center, and whose head strikes against the sun; at whose nod the princes of the earth shake their knees; pleasant as the spring, comfortable as the summer, fruitful as autumn, dreadful as winter. His most sublime Majesty proposeth to the Man-Mountain the following articles, which, by a solemn oath, he shall be obliged to perform:

"1st. The Man-Mountain shall not depart from our dominions without our license under our great seal.

"2nd. He shall not presume to come into our metropolis without our express order; at which time the inhabitants shall have two-hours' warning to keep within their doors.

"3rd. The Man-Mountain shall confine his walks to our high roads, and not walk or lie down in a meadow or field of corn.

"4th. As he walks the said roads, he shall take the utmost care not to trample upon the bodies of any of our loving subjects, their horses, or carriages, nor take any of our subjects into his hands without their own consent.

"5th. If an express requires extraordinary dispatch, the Man-Mountain shall be obliged to carry in his pocket the messenger and horse a six-days' journey once in every moon, and return the said messenger back (if it be so required) safe to our imperial presence.

"6th. He shall be our ally against our enemies in the Island of Blefuscu, and do his utmost to destroy their fleet, which is now preparing to invade us.

"7th. The said Man-Mountain shall be aiding and assisting to our workmen, in helping to raise certain great stones, toward covering the wall of the principal park, and other royal buildings.

"8th. The said Man-Mountain shall, in two-moons' time, deliver in an exact survey of the circumference of our dominions, by a computation of his own paces round the coast.

"Lastly. Upon his solemn oath to observe all the above articles, the said Man-Mountain shall have a daily allowance of meat and drink sufficient for the support of 1,724 of our subjects, with free access to our royal person, and other marks of our favour. Given at our palace at Belfaborac, the twelfth day of the ninety-first moon of our reign."

I swore and subscribed to these articles with great cheerfulness and content, whereupon my chains were immediately unlocked and I was at full liberty. The Emperor, himself, in person did me the honour to be by at the whole ceremony. I made my acknowledgments by prostrating myself at his Majesty's feet, but he commanded me to rise; and, after many gracious expressions, he added that he hoped I should prove a useful servant and well deserve all the favours he had already conferred upon me, or might do for the future.

The first request I made, after I had obtained my liberty, was that I might have license to see Mildendo, the metropolis, which the Emperor easily granted me, but with a special charge to do no hurt either to the inhabitants or their houses. The people had notice by proclamation of my design to visit the town. The wall which encompassed it is two feet and a half high, and at least eleven inches broad, so that a coach and horses may be driven very safely round it; and it is flanked with strong towers.

I stepped over the great Western Gate, and passed very gently and sideling through the two principal streets, only in my short waistcoat for fear of damaging the roofs and eaves of the houses with the skirts of my coat. I walked with the utmost circumspection to avoid treading on any stragglers that might remain in the streets, although the orders were strict that all people should keep in their houses at their own peril. The garret windows and tops of houses were so crowded with spectators that I thought, in all my travels, I had not seen a more populous place. The city is an exact square, each side of the wall being five-hundred feet long. The two great streets, which run across and divide it into four quarters, are five feet wide. The lanes and alleys, which I could not enter but only viewed them as I passed, are from twelve to eighteen inches. The houses are from three to five stories; the shops and markets well-provided.

The Emperor's palace is in the centre of the city, where the two great streets meet. It is inclosed by a wall of two feet high, and twenty feet distance from the buildings. I had his Majesty's permission to step over this wall; and, the space being so wide between that and the palace, I could easily view it on every side. The outward court is a square of forty feet, and includes two other courts. In the inmost are the royal apartments which I was very desirous to see, but found it extremely difficult, for the great gates, from one square into another, were but eighteen inches high and seven inches wide.

Now, the buildings of the outer court were at least five feet high, and it was impossible for me to stride over them without infinite damage to the pile, though the walls were strongly built of hewn stone, and four inches thick. At the same time, the Emperor had a great desire that I should see the magnificence of his palace; but this I was not able to do till three days after, which I spent in cutting down with my knife some of the largest trees in the royal park about an hundred yards distance from the city. Of these trees I made two stools, each about three feet high and strong enough to bear my weight. The people having received notice a second time, I went again through the city to the palace, with my two stools in my hands.

When I came to the side of the outer court, I stood upon one stool and took the other in my hand; this I lifted over the roof and gently set it down on the space between the first and second court, which was eight feet wide. I then stepped over the building very conveniently from one stool to the other and drew up the first after me with a hooked stick. By this contrivance I got into the inmost court; and, lying down upon my side, I applied my face to the windows of the middle stories, which were left open on purpose and discovered the most splendid apartments that can be imagined. There I saw the Empress and the young Princes, in their several lodgings, with their chief attendants about them. Her Imperial Majesty was pleased to smile very graciously upon me, and gave me out of the window her hand to kiss.

One morning about a fortnight after I had obtained my liberty, Reldresal, principal secretary of private affairs, came to my house. I offered to lie down, that he might the more conveniently reach my ear, but he chose to let me hold him in my hand during our conversation. He began with compliments on my liberty, but added that if it had not been for the present situation of things at court, I might not have obtained it so soon.

"For," said he, "as flourishing a condition as we may appear to be in to foreigners, we labour under two mighty evils, a violent faction at home and the danger of invasion by a potent enemy from abroad. As to the first, you are to understand that, for above seventy moons past, there have been two struggling parties in this empire, under the names of Tramecksan and Slamecksan, from the high and low heels of their shoes by which they distinguish themselves.

"It is alleged indeed that the high heels are most agreeable to our ancient constitution, but, however this be, his Majesty hath determined to make use of only low heels in the administration of the government, and all offices in the gift of the crown, and particularly, that his Majesty's imperial heels are lower at least by a drurr than any of his court (drurr is a measure about the fourteenth part of an inch). The animosities between these two parties run so high that they will neither eat nor drink nor talk with each other. We compute the Tramecksan, or high heels, to exceed us in number; but the power is wholly on our side. We apprehend his Imperial Highness, the heir to the crown, to have some tendency toward the high heels; at least, we can plainly discover that one of his heels is higher than the other, which gives him a hobble in his gait.

"Now, in the midst of these intestine disquiets, we are threatened with an invasion from the island of Blefuscu, which is the other great empire of the universe, almost as large and powerful as this of his Majesty. For as to what you affirm, that there are other kingdoms in the world inhabited by human creatures as large as yourself, our philosophers are in much doubt and would rather conjecture that you dropped from the moon or one of the stars. Besides, our histories make no mention of any other regions than the two great empires of Lilliput and Blefuscu, which two mighty powers have, as I was going to tell you, been engaged in a most obstinate war for six-and-thirty moons past.

"It began upon the following occasion. It is allowed on all

hands that the primitive way of breaking eggs before we eat them was upon the larger end; but his present Majesty's grandfather, while he was a boy breaking an egg according to the ancient practice, happened to cut one of his fingers. Whereupon the Emperor, his father, published an edict commanding all his subjects, upon great penalties, to break the smaller end of their eggs. The people so highly resented this law that, our histories tell us, there have been six rebellions on that account, wherein one emperor lost his life and another his crown.

"These civil commotions were constantly fomented by the monarchs of Blefuscu; and, when they were quelled, the exiles always fled for refuge to that empire. It is computed that eleven-thousand persons have suffered death rather than submit to break their eggs at the smaller end. Many hundred volumes have been published upon this controversy, but the books of the Big-endians have been long forbidden and the whole party rendered incapable by law of holding employments.

"The emperors of Blefuscu did frequently expostulate by their ambassadors, accusing us of making a schism in religion by offending against a fundamental doctrine of our great Prophet Lustrog, in the fifty-fourth chapter of the Blundecral (which is their Alcoran). This, however, is thought to be a strain upon the text for the words are these: 'That all true believers break their eggs at the convenient end.' And which is the convenient end seems, in my humble opinion, to be left to every man's conscience. Now, the Big-endian exiles have found so much credit in the Emperor of Blefuscu's court and so much private assistance from their party here at home, that a bloody war hath been carried on between the two empires for thirty-six moons. They have now equipped a numerous fleet and are preparing to make a descent upon us, and his Imperial Majesty, placing great confidence in your valor and strength, hath commanded me to lay this account of his affairs before you."

I desired the secretary to present my humble duty to the Emperor and let him know that I thought it would not become me, a foreigner, to interfere with parties; but I was ready, with the hazard of my life, to defend his person and state against all invaders.

The empire of Blefuscu is an island, situated to the northeast of Lilliput, from whence it is parted by a channel of eight-hundred yards wide. I communicated to his Majesty a project I had formed of seizing the enemy's whole fleet; which, as our scouts assured us, lay at anchor in the harbour ready to sail with the first fair wind. I walked toward the northeast coast, over against Blefuscu; where, lying down behind a hillock, I took out my perspective glass and viewed the enemy's fleet, consisting of about fifty men-of-war and a number of transports. I then came back to my house and gave order for a quantity of the strongest cable and bars of iron. The cable was about as thick as packthread, and bars of the size of a knitting needle. I trebled the cable to make it stronger and I twisted three of the iron bars together, binding the extremities into a hook. Having thus fixed fifty hooks to as many cables, I went back to the coast and putting off my coat, shoes, and stockings, walked into the sea, in my leathern jerkin, about an hour before high water. I waded with what haste I could and swam in the middle, till I felt ground. I arrived to the fleet in less than half an hour.

The enemy was so frightened when they saw me, that they leaped out of their ships and swam to the shore. I then took my tackling, and, fastening a hook to the hole at the prow of each ship, I tied all the cords together at the end. While I was thus employed, the enemy discharged several thousand arrows, many of which stuck in my hands and face and gave me much disturbance. My greatest apprehension was for mine eyes, which I should have lost, if I had not suddenly thought of an expedient. I kept a pair of spectacles in a private pocket, which, as I observed before, had escaped the Emperor's searchers. These I took out and fastened as strongly as I could upon my nose, and thus armed, went on boldly with my work in spite of the enemy's arrows.

I had now fastened all the hooks, and, taking the knot in my hand, began to pull, but not a ship would stir for they were fast held by their anchors. I, therefore, let go the cord and leaving the hooks fixed to the ships, I resolutely cut with my knife the cables that fastened the anchors, receiving about two-hundred shots in my face and hands. Then I took the knotted end of the cables to which my hooks were tied and, with great ease, drew fifty of the enemy's largest men-of-war after me. Waiting till the tide was a little fallen, I waded through the middle with my cargo and arrived safe at the royal port of Lilliput.

The Emperor and his whole court stood on the shore expecting the issue of this great adventure. They saw the ships move forward in a large half-moon, but could not discern me, who was up to my breast in water. When I was advanced to the middle of the channel, they were yet in more pain, because I was under water to my neck. The Emperor concluded me to be drowned, and that the enemy's fleet was approaching in a hostile manner, but he was soon eased of his fears for the channel growing shallower every step I made, I came in a short time within hearing, and, holding up the end of the cable by which the fleet was fastened, I cried in a loud voice, "Long live the most puissant Emperor of Lilliput!"

This great prince received me at my landing with all possible encomiums, and created me a *nardac* upon the spot, which is the highest title of honour among them.

His majesty desired I would take some other opportunity of bringing all the rest of his enemy's ships into his ports. And so unmeasurable is the ambition of princes, that he seemed to think of nothing less than reducing the whole empire of Blefuscu into a province and governing it by a viceroy; of destroying the Big-endian exiles and compelling that people to break the smaller end of their eggs, by which he would remain the sole monarch of the whole world. But I endeavored to divert him from his designs by many arguments drawn from the topics of policy as well as justice, and plainly protested that I would never be an instrument of bringing a free and brave people into slavery. And, when the matter was debated in council, the wisest part of the ministry were of my opinion. This bold declaration was so opposite to the schemes and politics of his Imperial Majesty, that he could never forgive me. And from this time began an intrigue between his Majesty and a junto of ministers maliciously bent against me, which broke out in less than two months and had like to have ended in my utter destruction.

About three weeks after this exploit, there arrived a solemn embassy from Blefuscu, with humble offers of a peace; which was soon concluded upon conditions very advantageous to our Emperor. There were six ambassadors with a train of about five-hundred persons. When their treaty was finished, wherein I did them several good offices by the credit I now had at court, their Excellencies invited me to that kingdom in the Emperor, their master's name. I desired they would present my most humble respects to the Emperor, whose royal person I resolved to attend before I returned to my own country. Accordingly, the next time I had the honour to see our Emperor, I desired his license to wait on the Blefuscudian monarch, which he was pleased to grant me, as I could plainly perceive, in a very cold manner but could not guess the reason, till I had a whisper from a certain person that Flimnap, the High-Treasurer, and Bolgolam, the Admiral, had represented my intercourse with those ambassadors as a mark of disaffection from which I am sure my heart was wholly free.

When I was just preparing to pay my attendance on the Emperor of Blefuscu, a considerable person at court came to my house very privately at night in a close chair, and, without sending his name, desired admittance. The chairmen were dismissed. I put the chair, with his lordship in it, into my coat pocket; and, giving orders to a trusty servant to say I was gone to sleep, I fastened the door of my house, placed the chair on the table, and sat down by it. Observing his lordship's countenance full of concern and enquiring into the reason, he desired I would hear him with patience, in a matter that highly concerned my honour and my life. His speech was to the following effect:

"You are very sensible that Skyresh Bolgolam (galbet, or high-admiral) hath been your mortal enemy almost ever since your arrival. His hatred is increased since your great success against Blefuscu, by which his glory as admiral is much obscured. This lord, in conjunction with Flimnap, the high-treasurer;

Limtoc, the general; Lalcon, the chamberlain; and Balmuff, the grand justiciary have prepared articles of impeachment against you for treason and other capital crimes. Out of gratitute for the favours you have done me, I procured a copy of the articles, wherein I venture my head for your service.

Article I: " 'The said Quinbus Flestrin (Man-Mountain) having brought the imperial fleet of Blefuscu into the royal port, and being commanded by his Imperial Majesty to seize all the other ships of the said empire and to destroy and put to death not only all the Big-endian exiles, but likewise all the people of that empire who would not forsake the Big-endian heresy; he, the said Flestrin, like a false traitor against his most auspicious, serene, Imperial Majesty, did petition to be excused from the said service, upon pretence of unwillingness to force the consciences, or destroy the liberties and lives of innocent people.

Article II: " 'Whereas certain ambassadors arrived from the court of Blefuscu, to sue for peace in his Majesty's court; he, the said Flestrin, did, like a false traitor, aid, abet, comfort, and divert the said ambassadors, although he knew them to be servants to a prince who was lately an open enemy to his Imperial Majesty.'

Article III: " 'The said Quinbus Flestrin, contrary to the duty of a faithful subject, is now preparing to make a voyage to the court and empire of Blefuscu and doth falsely and traitorously intend to aid, comfort, and abet the Emperor of Blefuscu.' "

"The treasurer and admiral insisted that you should be put to death by setting fire on your house at night, and the general was to attend with twenty-thousand men armed with poisoned arrows, to shoot you on the face and hands. Some of your servants were to have private orders to strew a poisonous juice on your shirts and sheets, which would soon make you tear your own flesh and die in the utmost torture. For a long time, there was majority against you; but his Majesty resolving, if possible, to spare your life, at last brought off the chamberlain.

"In three days, your friend, the secretary, will be directed to come to your house, to signify the great lenity and favour of his Majesty and council, whereby you are only condemned to the loss of your eyes, which his Majesty doth not question you will gratefully and humbly submit to. Twenty of his Majesty's surgeons will attend, in order to see the operation well-performed, by discharging very sharp-pointed arrows into the balls of your eyes as you lie on the ground. I leave to your prudence what measures you will take; and, to avoid suspicion, I must immediately return in as private manner as I came."

His lordship did so, and I remained alone, under many doubts and perplexities of mind. Once I was strongly bent upon resistance; but hurried on by the precipitancy of youth, I took the opportunity to send a letter to my friend the secretary, signifying my resolution of setting out that morning for Blefuscu, pursuant to the leave I had got. And, without waiting for an answer, I went to that side of the island where our fleet lay. I seized a large man-of-war, tied a cable to the prow, and, lifting up the anchors, I stripped myself, put my clothes into the vessel, and, drawing it after me, between wading and swimming, arrived at the royal port of Blefuscu, where the people had long expected me. They lent me two guides to direct me to the capital city. I held them in my hands till I came within two-hundred yards of the gate, and desired them to signify I there waited his Majesty's command. I had an answer in about an hour, that his Majesty, attended by the royal family and great officers of the court, was coming out to receive me. I advanced a hundred yards. The Emperor and his train alighted from their horses, the Empress and ladies from their coaches. I lay on the ground to kiss his Majesty's and the Empress's hands. I told his Majesty that I was come according to my promise and with the license of the Emperor, my master, not mentioning a word of my disgrace, because I had hitherto no regular information of it.

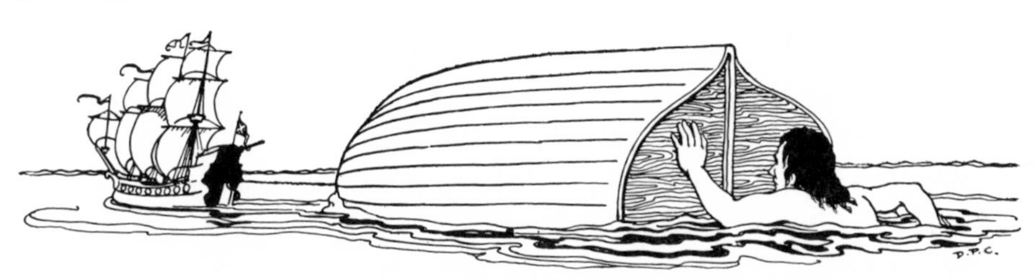

I shall not trouble the reader with the account of my reception at this court, which was suitable to the generosity of so great a prince. Three days after my arrival, walking out of curiosity to the northeast coast of the island, I observed, about half a league off, in the sea, somewhat that looked like a boat overturned. Wading two- or three-hundred yards, I found the object to be a real boat, which I supposed might, by some tempest, have been driven from a ship. Whereupon I returned toward the city and desired his Imperial Majesty to lend me twenty of the tallest vessels he had left after the loss of his fleet. This fleet sailed round, while I went back the shortest way to the coast. The seamen were all provided with cordage, which I had beforehand twisted to a sufficient strength. When the ships came up, I stripped myself and waded till I came within an hundred yards of the boat, after which I was forced to swim till I got up to it. The seamen threw me the end of the cord, which I fastened to a hole in the forepart of the boat and the other end to a man-of-war. I was forced to swim behind, and push the boat forward till the sea was no higher than my armpits. And now I took out my other cables, which were stowed in one of the ships, and fastened them first to the boat and then to nine of the vessels which attended me. The wind being favourable, the seamen towed and I shoved till we arrived within forty yards of the shore, and, waiting till the tide was out, I got dry to the boat; and, by the assistance of two-thousand men with ropes and engines, I made a shift to turn it on its bottom, and found it was but little damaged.

By the help of certain paddles, which cost me ten-days' making, I got my boat to the royal port of Blefuscu, where a mighty concourse of people appeared full of wonder at the sight of so prodigious a vessel. I told the Emperor that my good fortune had thrown this boat in my way to carry me to some place from whence I might return to my native country, and begged his Majesty's orders for getting materials to fit it up, together with his license to depart, which he was pleased to grant.

I did very much wonder, in all this time, not to have heard of any express relating to me from our Emperor to the court of Blefuscu. But I was afterward given privately to understand that his Imperial Majesty, never imagining I had the least notice of his designs, believed I was only gone to Blefuscu in performance of my promise, and would return in a few days when the ceremony was ended. But he was at last in pain at my long absence; and, a person of quality was dispatched with the copy of the articles against me. This envoy had instructions to represent to the monarch of Blefuscu the great lenity of his master, who was content to punish me no farther than with the loss of my eyes; that I had fled from justice, and if I did not return in two hours, should be deprived of my title of *nadac*, and declared a traitor. The envoy further added that in order to maintain the peace and amity between both empires, his master expected that his brother of Blefuscu would give orders to have me sent back to Lilliput, bound hand and foot, to be punished as a traitor.

The Emperor of Blefuscu returned an answer consisting of civilities and excuses. He said that as for sending me bound, his brother knew it was impossible; that although I had deprived him of his fleet, he owed great obligations to me for many good offices I had done him in making the peace; that both their Majesties would soon be made easy; for I had found a prodigious vessel, able to carry me on the sea, and he hoped, in a few weeks, both empires would be freed from so insupportable an incumbrance.

With this answer, the envoy returned to Lilliput; and the monarch of Blefuscu related to me all that had passed, offering me his gracious protection if I would continue in his service; wherein, although I believed him sincere, yet I resolved never more to put any confidence in princes or ministers. Therefore, I humbly begged to be excused. I told him that I was resolved to venture myself in the ocean rather than be an occasion of difference between two such mighty monarchs. Neither did I find the Emperor at all displeased, and I discovered, by accident, that he was very glad of my resolution and so were most of his ministers.

Five-hundred workmen were employed to make two sails to my boat by quilting thirteen-fold of their strongest linen together. I was at the pains of making ropes and cables by twisting ten, twenty, or thirty of the thickest and strongest of theirs. A great stone that I happened to find by the seashore, served me for an anchor. I had the tallow of three-hundred cows for greasing my boat and other uses. I was at incredible pains in cutting down some of the largest timber-trees for oars and masts, wherein I was much assisted by his Majesty's ship carpenters.

When all was prepared, I sent to receive his Majesty's commands and to take my leave. The Emperor and royal family came out of the palace; I lay down on my face to kiss his hand, which he graciously gave me; so did the Empress and princes of the blood. His Majesty presented me with fifty purses of two-hundred sprugs apiece, together with his picture at full length, which I put into one of my gloves, to keep it from being hurt.

I stored the boat with carcasses of an hundred oxen and three-hundred sheep, with bread and drink proportionable and as much meat ready dressed as four-hundred cooks could provide. I took six cows and two bulls alive, with as many ewes and rams, intending to carry them to my own country and propagate and breed. I would gladly have taken a dozen natives, but this the Emperor would by no means permit; and, besides a diligent search into my pockets, his Majesty engaged my honour not to carry away any of his subjects, although with their own consent and desire.

Having thus prepared all things, I set sail on the twenty-fourth day of September, 1701, at six in the morning; and, at six in the evening, I descried a small island about half a league to the northwest. I advanced forward and cast anchor on the lee-side of the island which seemed to be uninhabited. I then took some refreshment and went to my rest. I ate my breakfast before the sun was up, and heaving anchor, I steered the same course that I had done the day before, wherein I was directed by my pocket-compass. I discovered nothing all that day, but upon the next, about three in the afternoon, I descried a sail steering to the southeast. I hailed her, but could get no answer; yet I found I gained upon her, for the wind slackened. I made all the sail I could, and in half an hour she spied me and discharged a gun. It is not easy to express the joy I was in upon the unexpected hope of once more seeing my beloved country, and the dear pledges I had left in it. The ship slackened her sails, and I came up with her between five and six in the evening, September 26; but my heart leaped within me to see her English colours. I put my cows and sheep into my coat pockets and got on board with all my little cargo of provisions. The vessel was an English merchant-man returning from Japan.

There were about fifty men in the ship; and here I met an old comrade of mine, one Peter Williams, who gave me a good character to the captain. This gentleman treated me with kindness and desired I would let him know what place I came from last which I did in few words, but he thought I was raving and that the dangers I underwent had disturbed my head, whereupon I took my black cattle and sheep out of my pocket, which, after great astonishment, clearly convinced him of my veracity. I then showed him the gold given me by the Emperor of Blefuscu, together with his Majesty's picture at full length. I gave him two

purses of two-hundred sprugs each and promised, when we arrived in England, to make him a present of a cow and a sheep.

I shall not trouble the reader with a particular account of this voyage. We arrived in the Downs on the 13th of April, 1702. I had only one misfortune, that the rats on board carried away one of my sheep. I found her bones picked clean; neither could I possibly have preserved my cattle in so long a voyage if the captain had not allowed me some of his biscuit, which rubbed to powder and mingled with water, was their constant food. The short time I continued in England, I made a considerable profit of my showing cattle to persons of quality and others. Before I began my second voyage, I sold them for six-hundred pounds. Since my last return, I find the breed is considerably increased, especially the sheep, which I hope will prove much to the advantage of the woollen manufacture by the fineness of the fleeces.

Painting from the Collection of the John Hancock Mutual Life Ins. Co.

JOHN PAUL JONES, the First American Naval Hero

It was one of the most famous sea battles in history—this battle fought by Captain John Paul Jones in an unwieldy old ship, the *Bonhomme Richard.* Born in Scotland, Jones had sailed the seas since he was twelve. But after many adventures he had settled in Virginia, where he found Americans fighting for independence. And John Paul Jones believed in independence. So he had offered his services to the Continental Congress and been given command of the first little ship procured for the new-born American navy. In that ship and others equally small, for four years he had been doing tremendous damage to English shipping. On this day in September, 1779, he faced one of King George's most powerful warships in a worn out old trading ship, given him by the friendly French government.

On the *Bonhomme Richard*, Jones had been lying in wait off the English coast for England's great Baltic trade fleet, having with him only one small ship on whose commander he could rely, the French Ship, *Pallas.* When the fleet appeared, it consisted of 41 merchant vessels, escorted by the majestic *Serapis* and one smaller warship. It was evening when Jones intercepted the two warships. The *Pallas* took on the smaller ship and soon forced her surrender. But Jones had to meet the vastly superior *Serapis* in single combat. In the gathering dusk, he kept maneuvering the *Richard* closer and closer to her until he could use his grappling hooks and lash the two ships together. Then for three hours in the moonlight the fighting went on at close quarters. Two guns on the *Richard* burst, the dead were heaped high on her decks, she was on fire and having been hardly seaworthy to begin with, she was leaking so badly, she was nearly sinking, when Captain Pearson called out from the *Serapis,* demanding that Captain Jones should surrender.

"Surrender!" Jones boomed. "I haven't yet begun to fight!"

And he went on fighting, releasing prisoners from the hold to work the pumps and keep the *Richard* afloat. Men in the *Richard's* tops cleared the decks of the *Serapis* again and again. At last her mainmast threatened to fall. Pearson could do no more. He struck his flag and surrendered to Jones.

The Baltic fleet escaped and the *Richard,* her crew transferred to the *Serapis,* sank the next day. But this great victory, due entirely to the leadership and indomitable courage of John Paul Jones, the first great American naval commander, established firmly the traditions of the American navy.

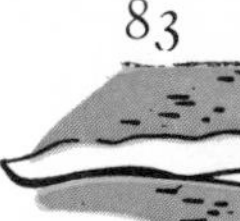

Young Midshipman David Farragut

WHEN the War of 1812 broke out, wherein the United States was compelled to fight England to establish her freedom on the seas, the frigate Essex was placed under the command of the renowned Captain David Porter. He came aboard bringing as midshipman his adopted son, David Farragut, who was one day to be known as America's greatest admiral. At the time he began his duties aboard the Essex David was ten years old.

Scarcely had the Essex put to sea when Captain Porter captured from the midst of a whole convoy of British transports a merchantman with two hundred men. Soon after that the Alert, a sloop of twenty guns, was taken. The two ships were taken in tow, but their officers and a number of the men were ordered aboard the Essex. Thus the Essex soon became dangerously overcrowded, her prisoners far outnumbering her crew members.

One night young David awoke to find a man with a pistol looming up above him. Instantly he guessed that there was a mutiny occuring among the prisoners. The man pointed the gun at David and watched to see if he was awake, but David lay still and kept his eyes closed. At last the Englishman was satisfied and stole away to join the other mutineers. Then David slipped silently out of his hammock and, keeping out of sight of the prisoners, went to warn Captain Porter. The Captain was asleep when the boy broke into his room, but he jumped instantly to his feet when he heard news of the mutiny. With remarkable keenness of wit, the Captain thought of a way to save the ship. Half dressed as he was, he rushed onto the deck shouting, "Fire! Fire! Fire!" The trick worked. Confused and alarmed, the mutineers stood dumbly by as the crew, well disciplined in fire drill, rushed to their stations, fully armed. This sudden appearance of the crew in fighting array so demoralized the mutineers that they were easily recaptured and taken below. Thus by his coolness and prompt action young Midshipman Farragut helped to save the ship. His next adventure at sea required a still greater display of calmness and courage.

Late in the winter of 1812 the Essex was ordered on a cruise through the South Atlantic around Cape Horn and into the Pacific, there to attack the extensive fishing interests of Great Britain, to rescue any American boats and to set free captured American whalers. The proper season for rounding Cape Horn had long since passed and the course of the Essex would lie through a region exceedingly tempestuous in winter. Moreover the ports along the coast were all friendly to England, and the Essex could not hope to refit or revictual in any of their harbors. She would have to depend solely on her own resources. Undaunted by the perils that lay before them, Captain Porter and his crew, little David Farragut among them, set out upon this distant cruise in the last days of January, 1813.

As the Essex neared the Horn, the most violent storms broke over her, lifting the waves into raging mountains of water and hurling them against the frail little boat with gigantic force. But in spite of all dangers and hardships she kept resolutely on. At length she sighted the rocky, barren shore of the Ga-lá pa-gos Islands off the coast of Ecuador, which Porter had learned were the favorite rendezvous for the British whalers. Here they cruised about, successfully capturing British whalers as they encountered them. Captain Porter eventually found himself with nine vessels under him and such a number of prisoners that he was obliged to send his prizes to the friendly port of Valparaiso, Chile, for safe keeping. To serve as escort for the convoy, one of the prizes was turned into a United States cruiser and christened the Essex Junior. She would accompany the captured vessels to Chile and then return to the Essex.

Captain Porter ordered each of his officers to command one of the captured ships as prizemaster, but there were not enough officers for all the ships. He found himself forced to select someone from among his crew to command the American ship Barclay, which he had recaptured from the British. For this responsible task his choice was Midshipman Farragut, who was then only twelve years old! It was a tremendously important duty, and the boy was rightfully proud of the confidence placed in him. With a party of seamen under his command, David was put aboard the Barclay with orders to accompany the convoy to Chile.

The Captain of the Barclay, who had been in command when the vessel was captured by the enemy, was a huge, violent-tempered old fellow, and he was furious at being superseded by a "nutshell of a boy." He determined to put the twelve-year-old boy in his place the moment the other ships had departed. Accordingly, when the Essex Junior and the convoy made off to southward, and Captain Porter had disappeared to the northward, the Captain of the Barclay still kept his vessel contemptuously at anchor, making no preparations to follow, and flaunting his intention of remaining where he was exactly so long as it pleased him.

Little Midshipman Farragut knew at once that the confrontation had come. He must now act like a man or else fail in his duty and yield up his command. Though he was secretly afraid of the grizzly old Captain, he nevertheless walked right up to him and ordered quietly: "Have the maintopsail filled away, and close up at once with the convoy."

At this the Captain burst forth in a fury. He would sail his ship wherever he pleased and whenever he pleased. No one

would make him sail to Chile against his will. And he cried out to the sailors standing about: "Let no man dare touch a rope without my orders. I'll shoot if you do. I'll go my own course and shoot the dog who takes orders from any but me." With that he plunged down the companionway to his cabin to get his pistols.

The men stood about irresolute. It was a tense moment. But without betraying the fear he felt, young Farragut turned to the crew. "Have the maintopsail filled away!" he repeated in a strong voice. His pluck turned the tide with the men and they flew into action.

"Aye, aye, sir," came the cheerful response.

After giving orders to make sail, David calmly notified the Captain below not to come on deck with his pistols unless he wished to go overboard! The Captain, perceiving that the crew remained faithful to David, and that David would have no difficulty in having him pitched into the sea, decided to obey. Thus, on the long voyage to Chile David was in command, and he carried out that great responsibility with skill, good judgment, and self-reliance.

After safely guiding the Barclay to Chile, David returned to the Galapagos Islands aboard the Essex Junior with the other prizemasters. Upon rejoining the Essex they informed Captain Porter of startling news that they had heard in Valparaiso. The British were so aroused by tales of the destruction the Essex had wrought that they were sending the frigate Phoebe and two sloops after her.

On hearing this, Captain Porter at once sailed westward to the Marquesas Islands where he could overhaul the Essex without danger from British men-of-war and could prepare for the coming struggle with a greatly superior force. Here the Essex and the Essex Junior lay for six months. The crews were daily drilled in the use of the guns, cutlasses, muskets, and were trained with the perfect discipline for which Captain Porter was famous.

When all preparations were made, the two ships proceeded to Valparaiso Harbor to await the Phoebe. In only five days she arrived. At the time, half the Essex's crew were ashore, and Captain Hillyar of the Phoebe determined to seize the Essex while her guard was down. He disregarded the fact that Valparaiso was a neutral harbor, where such hostile actions were unlawful. Captain Porter was ready, however, and the boom of his signal gun brought the crew back to the ship. When the Phoebe pulled alongside, Captain Hillyar found every American at his gun. In face of such a formidable state of defense he speedily backed away, trying to pass off his approach with some clumsy compliments to Captain Porter. In her haste to get away, the Phoebe placed herself in such a vulnerable position that the Essex could have sunk her on the spot. But Captain Porter would not violate the neutrality of the harbor, so he let the Phoebe go free. He later found that Captain Hillyar was not a man to return such a favor.

The English ships then began a blockade of the harbor. Week after week they cruised up and down just outside the bay.

On March twenty-eighth, a heavy gale swept into the harbor and Porter decided to take advantage of the weather to run the blockade. At first it looked as though he would succeed, but on her way the Essex was struck by a violent squall that carried away her maintopsail. Escape in such a disabled state was impossible, so Porter tried to regain his safe position in the harbor, but the Essex was only able to struggle as far back as a small bay about a quarter of a mile off shore. She was, however, still within neutral waters and had every reason to expect that Hillyar would respect that neutrality, remembering how Porter had refused to fire on him when he had the Phoebe so entirely at his mercy. But Porter soon saw his mistake. As soon as the British discerned the plight of the Essex, the three vessels bore down together on the crippled frigate, now separated from her companion, and opened their broadsides on her. Then began one of the most nobly contested defenses in history, the odds being from the beginning three to one against the Essex.

Through the frightful scenes that followed, Midshipman Farragut bore himself like a man, now carrying messages for Captain Porter, now helping with a gun, now fetching powder, now supporting a wounded man down below. Once he was knocked down a hatch by the explosion of a cannon ball. Again a shot tore away one of his coat-tails, but still the little midshipman remained at his post in the midst of the fray. At length fire broke out on the ship, and was nearing the powder magazine. Men came running up from below with their clothing on fire. Captain Porter ordered them to jump overboard and swim for their lives. Then, finding that the ship was in a sinking condition, he surrendered in order to save the wounded.

On the following day, David Farragut went aboard the Phoebe, a prisoner, and was sent into the steerage with the British middies. He was almost in tears over the capture of the Essex, but was roused from his grief by the sight of an English midshipman calmly appropriating his—David's—beloved pet pig Murphy.

"That's my pig!" shrieked David, seizing Murphy by the ear.

"Fight for it then!" jeered the others.

Without more ado David stripped off his jacket and pitched into the young Englishman in short order, with such excellent results that in a few moments he had most soundly and satisfactorily trounced him. Thereafter he took Master Murphy under his arm and walked off, feeling that he had thus in some degree wiped out the disgrace of the American defeat!

Soon after this, David was sent back to America with the other officers on parole, and thus ended his connection with the famous frigate Essex, whereon he got the training that years later in the war for the preservation of the American Union, made possible the splendid victories of New Orleans and Mobile Bay, victories won against almost impossible odds by the man that grew out of that self-same boy who was midshipman David Farragut.

A WANDERER'S SONG

JOHN MASEFIELD*

A WIND'S in the heart of me, a fire's in my heels,
I am tired of brick and stone and rumbling wagon-wheels;
I hunger for the sea's edge, the limits of the land,
Where the wild old Atlantic is shouting on the sand.

Oh, I'll be going, leaving the noises of the street,
To where a lifting foresail-foot is yanking at the sheet;
To a windy, tossing anchorage where yawls and ketches ride,
Oh, I'll be going, going, until I meet the tide.

And first I'll hear the sea-wind, the mewing of the gulls,
The clucking, sucking of the sea about the rusty hulls,
The songs at the capstan in the hooker warping out,
And then the heart of me'll know I'm there or thereabout.

Oh, I am tired of brick and stone, the heart of me is sick,
For windy green, unquiet sea, the realm of Moby Dick;
And I'll be going, going, from the roaring of the wheels,
For a wind's in the heart of me, a fire's in my heels.

*The lure of the sea made John Masefield a sailor at fourteen. The queenly stateliness of ships, yarns of sailors, and bounding rhythms of waves are in the work of this English poet laureate, born in 1875.

The Magic Horse

The Arabian Nights*

THROUGHOUT all Persia the Nevrouz, or Festival of the New Year, has always been celebrated with extraordinary rejoicings. Strangers are invited to appear at court and liberal rewards are given by the Sultan to those who can produce the most wonderful inventions. On one of these feast days, after the most skillful inventors of the country had displayed their devices before the Sultan of Persia at Schiraz, there suddenly appeared at the foot of the throne, just as the assembly was breaking up, a Hindu with an artificial horse. The horse was richly bridled and saddled and so wonderfully made that at first sight he looked like a living creature. The Hindu prostrated himself before the throne, and, pointing to the horse, said to the Sultan:

"Sire, of all wonders which you have this day seen, I assure you this horse is the most wonderful. Whenever I mount him, be it where it may, if I wish to transport myself to the most distant part of the world, I can do it in a very short time. This is a marvel which nobody ever heard of, and which I offer to display for your majesty if you command me."

The Sultan who was fond of everything that was curious, had indeed never beheld or heard of anything that came up to this, so he bade the Hindu perform what he had promised. The Hindu immediately put his foot into the stirrup, and mounted his horse with agility. When he had fixed himself in the saddle, he asked the Sultan where he was pleased to send him.

About three leagues from Schiraz there was a high mountain visible from the large square before the palace, where the Sultan and his court and a great concourse of people were then gathered.

"Do you see that mountain?" said the Sultan. "Ride your

**Arabian Nights* consists of old folk tales of India, Egypt, Arabia, and Persia. The first European translation was made in 1704, by a Frenchman, M. Galland. Edward W. Lane made the best English translation, in 1839.

horse thither and bring me a branch from the palm tree that grows at the bottom of the hill."

The Sultan had no sooner declared his will, than the Hindu turned a peg, which was in the hollow of the horse's neck, just by the pommel of the saddle. In an instant the horse rose off the ground and carried his rider into the air like lightning, rising to such a great height that the Sultan and all the spectators were struck with admiration. In less than a quarter of an hour they saw him returning with the palm branch in his hand. Before he descended, he took two or three turns in the air amid the acclamations of the people, then alighted on the spot whence he had set off. He dismounted, and prostrated himself before the throne, laying the branch of the palm tree at the feet of the Sultan.

The Sultan, who had viewed this unheard-of sight with no less admiration than astonishment, conceived a great desire to have the horse, and said to the Hindu: "I will buy him of you."

"Sire," replied the Hindu, "I beg of you not to be angry with me, but I cannot resign to you my horse, except on receiving the hand of the Princess, your daughter, as my wife."

The courtiers could not forbear laughing aloud at this extravagant demand of the Hindu; but the Prince Firouz Schah, the Sultan's eldest son, and heir to the crown, could not hear it without indignation. "Sire," he said, "I hope you will not hesitate to refuse so insolent a demand, or allow this insignificant juggler to flatter himself for a moment with the idea of being allied to one of the most powerful monarchs in the world."

"Son," replied the Sultan, "putting my daughter, the Princess, out of the question, I may still make another agreement with the Hindu. But before I bargain at all, I should be glad that you would examine the horse, try him yourself and give me your opinion." On hearing this, the Hindu readily ran before the prince to help him mount and show him how to guide and

In *Arabian Nights*, it is related how Scheherazade told these tales to entertain the cruel Sultan who threatened her life. Rimski-Korsakov, in "The Scheherazade Suite" pictures the Festival at Bagdad, and other tales she told.

manage the horse. But the Prince mounted without the Hindu's assistance; and as soon as he had his feet in the stirrups, without waiting for the artist's advice, he turned the peg he had seen him use. Instantly the horse darted up in the air quick as an arrow out of a bow. In a few moments neither horse nor Prince was to be seen.

The Hindu, alarmed at what had happened, prostrated himself before the throne and cried out: "Sire, your Majesty yourself saw that the Prince was so hasty he would not permit me to give him the necessary instructions how to govern my horse. He knows not how to turn the horse around and bring him back again. I beg you do not hold me accountable for what may happen to him." But the Sultan, perceiving the danger into which his son's impatience had brought him, asked in a passion why the Hindu had not called out instructions to the prince the moment he saw him ascend.

"Sire," answered the Hindu, "your Majesty saw as well as I with what rapidity the horse flew away. Surprise deprived me of the use of my tongue. But," he added, "there is reason to hope that the Prince when he finds himself at a loss, will perceive another peg; as soon as he turns that the horse will cease to rise, and descend to the ground, when he may turn him to what place he pleases by guiding him with the bridle."

"Your head shall answer for my son's life, if he does not return safe in three months' time," cried the Sultan, and he ordered his officers to secure the Hindu and keep him close prisoner; after which he retired to his palace in great affliction.

In the meantime, Prince Firouz Schah was carried through the air with prodigious swiftness, and in less than an hour's time he had got so high that he could not distinguish anything on the earth. Mountains and plains seemed confounded together. It was then he began to think of returning, and thought to do it by turning the same peg he had used before, only the contrary way, pulling the bridle at the same time. But when he found that the horse still continued to ascend, his alarm was great. He turned the peg several times, one way and the other, but all in vain. It was then he saw his fault, and apprehended the great danger he was in, from not having waited to learn how to guide the horse before he mounted. He examined the horse's head and neck with great attention, and at length perceived behind the right ear another peg, smaller than the first. He turned that peg, and immediately the horse began to descend in the

same oblique manner as he had mounted, but not so swiftly.

Night had overshadowed that part of the earth over which the prince was flying when he discovered the small peg; and as the horse descended, he by degrees lost sight of the sun till it grew quite dark, insomuch that, instead of choosing what place he would go to, he was obliged to let the bridle lie upon the horse's neck and wait patiently till he alighted, though not without dread lest it should be in the desert, a river or the sea.

At last, after midnight, the horse reached the ground and the Prince dismounted very faint and hungry, having eaten nothing since the morning when he came out of the palace with his father to assist at the festival. He found himself to be on the terrace of a magnificent palace surrounded with a balustrade of white marble breast high, and, groping about, reached a staircase.

None but Prince Firouz Schah would have ventured to go down those stairs, dark as they were, and exposed to danger. But he said to himself: "I do not come to do anybody any harm, so whoever meets me and finds me unarmed will attempt nothing against me without hearing what I have to say for myself." After this reflection he went softly down the stairs, and came to a landing place where he found a door opening into an apartment that had a light in it.

The Prince stopped and, listening, heard no other sound within than the snoring of some people who were fast asleep. He advanced a little into the room and by the light of the lamp saw that those persons were black chamberlains with naked sabres laid by them, which was enough to inform him that this was the guardchamber of some queen or princess. Prince Firouz Schah advanced on tip-toe, without waking the chamberlains and drew aside the silken curtain that hung before an inner room. There he saw a magnificent chamber containing many beds, one alone being on a raised dais and the others on the floor. The

Princess slept in the first and her women in the others. He crept softly toward the dais and there beheld a beauty so extraordinary that he was charmed at first sight. Gently he woke the Princess. She opened her eyes, and seeing a handsome young man, was in great surprise, yet showed no sign of fear.

The Prince bowed himself to the ground and said: "Beautiful Princess, by the most extraordinary and wonderful adventure, you see at your feet a suppliant Prince, son of the Sultan of Persia. Pray afford him your assistance and protection."

The personage to whom Firouz Schah so happily addressed himself was the Princess of Bengal, eldest daughter of the Rajah of that kingdom, who had built this palace at a small distance from his capital, whither she went to enjoy the country. After she had heard the Prince, she replied with kindness: "Prince, hospitality, humanity, and politeness are to be met with in the kingdom of Bengal, as well as in Persia. I grant you the protection you ask—you may depend on what I say." The Prince of Persia would have thanked the Princess of Bengal for her kindness, but she would not give him leave. "Notwithstanding my desire," said she, "to know by what miracle you have come hither from the capital of Persia in so short a time and how you have been able to come to my apartment and escape the vigilance of my guards, as you must want some refreshment, I will postpone my curiosity and give orders to my women to regale you, and show you to a room where you may rest after your fatigue."

The Princess' women each took a wax candle and after the Prince had taken leave very respectfully, they went before him and conducted him into a handsome chamber, where they brought him all sorts of meats. When he had eaten they left him to repose. In the meantime the Princess of Bengal was so struck with the intelligence, politeness, and other good qualities which she had discovered in that short conversation with the Prince, that she could not sleep, but when her women came into her room again, she asked them if they had taken care of him, and more particularly what they thought of him.

The women answered: "We do not know what you may think of him, but, for our part, we think you would be very happy if the Rajah, your father, would marry you to so amiable a prince, for there is not a prince in all the kingdom of Bengal to compare with him, nor can we hear that any of the neighboring princes are worthy of you."

Nothing went forward for several days following this but concerts of music, accompanied with magnificent feasts in the garden, or hunting parties in the vicinity of the palace, which abounded with all sorts of game, stags and deer, and other beasts peculiar to the kingdom of Bengal. After the chase, the Prince and Princess met in some beautiful spot, where a carpet was spread, and cushions laid for their accommodation. There, resting themselves, they conversed on various subjects.

For two whole months Prince Firouz Schah remained the guest of the Princess of Bengal, taking part in all the amusements she arranged for him. But after that time, he declared seriously that he could not stay any longer, and begged her to give him leave to return to his father, repeating a promise he had made to her to return soon in a style worthy of her and of himself to demand her in marriage of the Rajah.

"And, Princess," observed the Prince of Persia, "that you may not doubt the truth of my affection, I would presume, were I not afraid you would be offended at my request, to ask the favor of taking you along with me to visit my father, the Sultan."

The Princess returned no answer to this address of the Prince of Persia; but her silence and down-cast eyes were sufficient to inform him that she had no reluctance to accompany him into Persia. The next morning, therefore, a little before daybreak,

they went upon the terrace of the palace. The Prince turned the horse's head towards Persia, and the Princess was no sooner up behind him with her arms about his waist for better security, than he turned the peg, when the horse mounted into the air. In two hours' time, the Prince discovered the capital of Persia.

The Prince would not alight in the palace of his father, but directed his course toward a small kiosk at a little distance from the capital. He led the Princess into a handsome apartment where he told her that to do her all honor, he would go and inform his father of their arrival, and return to her immediately. He ordered the attendants of the palace whom he summoned to provide the Princess with whatever she had occasion for.

Having then taken leave of the Princess, he left the artificial horse and ordered a real one to be brought. This he mounted and set out for the palace. As he passed through the streets he was received with acclamations by the people, who were overjoyed to see him again. The Sultan his father was in the midst of his council when his son appeared before him. He received the Prince with tears of joy and, embracing him, asked what had been his adventures. This question gave the Prince an opportunity of describing what had happened to him and the affection he and the Princess of Bengal entertained for each other; also how he had persuaded her to accompany him into Persia and desired his father's consent to their marriage.

After these words the Sultan embraced his son a second time and said: "Son, I not only consent to your marriage with the Princess of Bengal, but will go and meet her myself, thank her for the obligation I am under to her, bring her to my palace and celebrate your wedding this day."

The Sultan now ordered that the Hindu should be fetched out of prison and brought before him, when he said: "Thanks be to God, my son is returned again. Go, take your horse and never let me see your face more."

As the Hindu had learned that Prince Firouz Schah was returned with a Princess whom he had left at the kiosk, he thought he would just be beforehand with the Prince and the Sultan and have the Princess for himself. So, without losing any time, he went direct to the kiosk, and addressing himself to the Captain of the Guard, told him he came from the Prince of Persia to fetch the Princess of Bengal on the horse to the Sultan, who waited in the great square of the palace to gratify the whole court and the city of Schiraz with that wonderful sight.

The Captain of the Guard credited what the Hindu said and presented him to the Princess of Bengal, who no sooner understood that he came from the Prince of Persia, than she consented to what the Prince, as she thought, desired of her.

The Hindu, overjoyed at the ease with which he had accomplished his villainy, mounted his horse, took the Princess before him and turned the peg, whereat the horse mounted instantly into the air.

At the same time, the Sultan, with his entire court, was on the way from his palace to the kiosk, and the Prince of Persia had ridden on before to prepare the Princess to receive his father. To defy them both and revenge himself for the ill-treatment he had received, the Hindu appeared directly over their heads with his prize. When the Sultan of Persia saw the Hindu he stopped. His surprise and affliction were keen. He loaded him with a thousand imprecations, as did also all his courtiers. But the Hindu, little moved by their curses, continued his way, while the Sultan went back to his palace in rage and vexation.

But what was Prince Firouz Schah's grief to see the Hindu carry away the Princess whom he loved so dearly! At so unexpected a sight he was thunderstruck, and before he could make up his mind what to do the horse was out of sight. He continued his way therefore to the kiosk where he had left the Princess. When he arrived, the Captain of the Guard, who had learned how he had been deceived, threw himself at the Prince's feet, and, with tears in his eyes, accused himself of the crime which he had unintentionally committed.

"Rise up," said the prince to him, "I do not impute the loss of my Princess to you, but to my own want of precaution. But lose no more time; fetch me a dervish's robe at once and take care that you do not give the least hint it is for me."

Not far from this place there stood a convent of dervishes, the superior of which was the particular friend of the Captain of the Guard. From him the Captain readily obtained a complete dervish's habit, and carried it to Prince Firouz Schah. The Prince immediately put it on, and being so disguised, left the palace, uncertain which way to go, but resolved never to return until he had found out his Princess.

Meantime, the Hindu, mounted on his enchanted horse with the Princess before him, arrived early that evening at the capital of the kingdom of Cashmere. Being hungry, he alighted in an open part of the wood, and left the Princess on a grassy spot, close to a rivulet of fresh water, while he went to seek for food. During the Hindu's absence, the Princess, knowing that she was in the power of a base deceiver, whose violence she dreaded, thought of getting away from him and seeking a sanctuary. But the Hindu discovered her, and dragged her back with great violence. The Princess made stout resistance and her cries and shrieks soon drew to the spot the Sultan of Cashmere and his attendants who chanced to be passing.

The Sultan, addressing himself to the Hindu, demanded who he was and wherefore he ill-treated the lady. The Hindu, with great impudence, replied that she was his wife, and what had anyone to do with his quarrel with her?

The Princess, who knew neither the rank nor the quality of the person who came so seasonably to her relief, exclaimed: "Sir, whoever you are whom Heaven has sent to my assistance, have compassion on a Princess, and give no credit to that impostor. He is a wicked magician who has stolen me away from the Prince of Persia to whom I was going to be married, and has brought me hither on the enchanted horse you behold there."

The Princess of Bengal had no occasion to say more. Her beauty, majestic air and tears, declared that she spoke the truth. Justly enraged at the insolence of the Hindu, the Sultan ordered his guards to surround him and strike off his head, which sentence was immediately executed. The Sultan then conducted the Princess to his palace, where he lodged her in the most magnificent apartment and commanded a great number of women slaves to attend her.

The Princess of Bengal's joy was inexpressible at finding herself delivered from the Hindu, of whom she could not think without horror. She flattered herself that the Sultan of Cashmere would complete his generosity by sending her back to the Prince of Persia when she should have told him her story and asked that favor of him. But she was much deceived in these hopes, for her deliverer had resolved to marry her himself the next day; and to that end had issued a proclamation, commanding the general rejoicing of the inhabitants of the capital. At the break of day, drums were beaten, trumpets sounded and the whole palace echoed with music and joy.

When the Sultan of Cashmere came to wait upon the Princess of Bengal, he informed her that all those rejoicings were in honor of their wedding; and at the same time, desired her to agree to the marriage. This declaration threw her into such a state of agitation that, rather than break the promise she had made to Prince Firouz Schah, by consenting to marry the Sultan of Cashmere, she resolved to feign madness. She began to utter the most extravagant expressions before the Sultan and ever rose off her seat as if to fly at him; insomuch that the Sultan was very much surprised and greatly afflicted that he should have made his proposal so unseasonably.

When he found that her frenzy rather increased than abated, he left her with her women, charging them never to leave her alone, but to take great care of her. He sent often that day, to inquire how she did, but received no other answer than that she was rather worse than better. So the Sultan was induced to send for all the physicians about his court to ask if they could cure her. When he saw that they could not, he called in the most celebrated and experienced physicians of the city who had no better success. He then sent for the most famous in the kingdom and to neighboring courts, but all with no effect.

During this interval, Firouz Schah disguised in the habit of a dervish, had traveled through a great many provinces and towns, full of grief and having endured much fatigue, not knowing which way to direct his course. He made diligent inquiry after his lost Princess at every place he came to. At last, passing through a city of Hindustan, he heard the people talk much of a Princess of Bengal who had become mad on the day of her intended marriage to the Sultan of Cashmere. Supposing that there could exist no other Princess of Bengal, he had hastened toward the kingdom of Cashmere, and upon his arrival at the capital, took up his lodging at a khan, where, the same day, he was informed of the story of the Princess and the fate of the Hindu magician. The Prince was convinced he had at last found the beloved object whom he had sought so long.

Being informed of all particulars, he provided himself with a physician's habit and went boldly to the palace, announcing to the chief of the officers his wish to be allowed to undertake the cure of the Princess. Some time had elapsed since any physician had offered himself; and the Sultan of Cashmere had begun to lose all hope of ever seeing the Princess restored to herself.

Therefore he lost no time in ordering the officer to introduce the new physician. The Sultan then told the Prince that the Princess of Bengal could not bear the sight of a physician without falling into the most violent transports. Accordingly, he conducted the Prince into a closet whence he might see her without being observed. There Firouz Schah beheld his lovely Princess looking very melancholy and singing an air in which she deplored the unhappy fate which had deprived her perhaps forever of the prince whom she loved so tenderly.

The Prince was much affected at the melancholy condition in which he found his beloved Princess, but he at once comprehended that her madness was but a pretence. When he came away, he told the Sultan that he had discovered the nature of her ailment, but added that, in spite of the manner in which she took on at sight of a physician, he must speak to her in private.

The Sultan ordered the Princess' door to be opened and Firouz Schah went in. As soon as the Princess saw him, she resorted to her old practice of violence on meeting physicians, but he made directly toward her, and when he was nigh enough for her to hear, and no one else, he said in a low voice: "Princess, I am not a physician, but the Prince of Persia."

The Princess, who knew the sound of his voice and recognized his features, notwithstanding he had let his beard grow long, became calm at once and a secret joy and pleasure overspread her face. Firouz Schah then told her as briefly as possible his own adventures and she informed him of all that had happened to her—how she had feigned to be mad because she saw no other way to preserve herself for a prince to whom she had given her heart and faith. The Prince of Persia then asked her if she knew what had become of the horse, to which she answered that she did not, but she supposed, after the account she had given the sultan of it, he would preserve it as a curiosity.

The Sultan of Cashmere was overjoyed when the Prince of Persia stated to him how calmly the Princess had received him and what effect his first visit had had toward her recovery. In order to introduce the subject of the horse, the Prince then inquired of the Sultan how the Princess had come into the kingdom of Cashmere thus alone, when her own country was so far distant. The Sultan at once informed him; adding that he had ordered the horse to be kept safe, though he knew not how to use it.

"Sire," replied Firouz Schah, "the information which your majesty has given me affords me a means of restoring the Princess. As she was brought hither on this horse and the horse is enchanted she hath contracted somewhat of the enchantment, which can be dissipated only by a certain incense I know of. If your majesty would entertain yourself, your court, and the people of your capital with the most surprising sight that ever you beheld, let the horse be brought tomorrow into the great square before the palace, and leave the rest to me. I promise to show you and all that assembly in a few moments, the Princess of Bengal completely recovered."

The Sultan would have undertaken much more difficult things to have secured his marriage with the Princess, moreover he was greatly encouraged by the improvement already made, so, the next day, the enchanted horse was by his order taken out of the treasury, and placed in the great square before the palace. A report was spread through the town that there was something extraordinary to be seen, and crowds of people flocked thither from all parts, insomuch that the Sultan's guards were placed about to prevent disorder, and to keep space enough round the horse.

The Sultan of Cashmere, surrounded by all his nobles and ministers of state, was placed in a gallery erected on purpose. The Princess of Bengal, attended by a number of women whom the Sultan had assigned to her, went up to the enchanted horse, and the women helped her to mount. When she was fixed in the saddle and had the bridle in her hand, the Prince of Persia placed round the horse, at a proper distance, many vessels full of lighted charcoal, which he had ordered to be brought, and going round them with a solemn pace, cast in handfuls of incense. Then, with downcast eyes and his hands upon his breast, he ran three times about the horse, making as if he pronounced some mystical words. The moment the pots sent forth a dark cloud of smoke accompanied with a pleasant smell,—which so surrounded the Princess that neither she nor the horse was to be discerned,—the Prince, watching his opportunity, jumped nimbly up behind her, and reaching his hand to the peg, turned it. Just as the horse rose with them into the air, he pronounced these words which the Sultan heard distinctly: "Sultan of Cashmere, when you would marry a Princess who implores your protection, learn first to obtain her consent."

Thus the Prince delivered the Princess of Bengal, and carried her the same day to the capital of Persia, where he alighted in the midst of the palace before the window of the Sultan, his father.

The Sultan deferred the marriage only so long as was required to make preparations to render the ceremony magnificent.

After the days appointed for the rejoicing were over, the Sultan of Persia at once sent an ambassador to the Rajah of Bengal, to give him an account of what had happened and ask his approval of the marriage. This the Rajah of Bengal took as an honor and was pleased to grant with great satisfaction.

RECOLLECTIONS OF THE ARABIAN NIGHTS

ALFRED TENNYSON

When the breeze of a joyful dawn blew free
In the silken sail of infancy,
The tide of time flowed back with me,
The forward-flowing tide of time;
And many a sheeny summer-morn,
Adown the Tigris I was borne,
By Bagdad's shrines of fretted gold,
High-walled gardens green and old;
True Mussulman was I and sworn,
For it was in the golden prime
Of good Ha-roun′ Al-rasch′id.

Anight my shallop, rustling through
The low and bloomed foliage, drove
The fragrant, glistening deeps, and clove
The citron-shadows in the blue:
By garden porches on the brim,
The costly doors flung open wide,
Gold glittering through lamp light dim,
And broidered sofas on each side;
In sooth it was a goodly time,
For it was in the golden prime
Of good Ha-roun′ Al-rasch′id.

The Story of the Talking Bird

The Arabian Nights

There were once two brothers named Bah′man and Per′viz, who lived in Persia in the closest and most pleasant friendship with their only sister Par′i-zade. They had never known their father, the Sultan Khos′roo Shah, nor he them, for they had been stolen away from the palace one after the other when they were but a day old. Now, on the occasion when the Sultan had asked to see his first babe, two wicked aunts, who lived in the palace, and had a spite against their sister, the Sultaness, told him that the Sultaness had in the cradle but a puppy, which she was trying to pass off as a child; on the second occasion that she had a cat, on the third a log of wood and no real infant at all, which ridiculous tale the Sultan was foolish enough to believe, conceiving, finally, such indignation against the Sultaness that he ordered her to be imprisoned in a shed with iron bars to the windows near one of the great mosques. But the truth of the matter was that the aunts had stolen the real babes, substituting for each in turn a dog, a cat, and a log of wood. They placed the children each in a basket, and sent them, one after the other, adrift down the canal.

It so happened that, just after the first babe was sent adrift, the keeper of the Sultan's gardens, a powerful but kind-hearted officer, who lived on the canal bank some way below the palace, was walking along the path and saw something floating in the water. He called to the gardener, who came with his rake, reached out toward the floating object, and drew it to land. To their great surprise they found it to be a basket containing a beautiful little boy. The keeper, to his sorrow, had no children of his own, so he immediately determined to adopt this foundling, and picking up the basket, carried the babe to his wife, who received the child with great joy and named him Bahman.

The following year, the keeper while walking on the canal banks, saw another floating basket, containing another babe, whom he and his wife adopted in exactly the same way, and named Perviz. The third year there appeared a third basket containing the little Princess, whom they called Parizade and brought up with the boys. The keeper and his wife grew so extremely fond of these children, that they determined not to make any inquiries into the mystery of their origin, nor to tell them that they were not really their own. All of them were so quick and clever and good that the keeper had them taught by the very best masters, and although the sister was the youngest, she was soon as proficient in all learning, in riding, running, bending the bow and darting the javelin as her brothers, whom indeed she oftentimes outdid in the race or other contest of agility.

The keeper was so overjoyed to find his adopted children so accomplished in body and mind, and so well justifying the care and expense he had bestowed upon them, that he determined to build them a country house at some distance from the city, and to furnish it most magnificently. He then asked permission of the sultan to be released from his service as he wished to end his days in peace and tranquillity. The sultan granted this request, with the more pleasure because he was satisfied with his long services, and the keeper retired with the two princes and the princess to the country retreat he had built. His wife had now been dead some years, and the keeper himself had not lived above six months with his charges, before he, too, suddenly died without ever giving the Princes and the Princess any account of the manner in which he had found them.

The Princes Bahman and Perviz, and the Princess Parizade, who knew no other father and loved the keeper as such, paid his memory all the honors which love and filial gratitude required of them. Content with the plentiful fortune he had left them, they lived together in perfect union, free from any ambition for places of honor and dignity at court.

One day when the two Princes were hunting, and the Princess Parizade stayed at home, an old woman came to the gate and desired leave to come in and say her prayers, it being then the hour. The servants asked the Princess' permission, who ordered them to show her into the oratory.

The old woman went into the oratory and when she came out, two of the Princess' women invited her to see the residence, which civility she accepted, following them from one apartment to another and observing the nice arrangement of everything. Afterward she was brought before the Princess in the great hall.

As soon as the Princess saw the old woman, she said to her: "My good mother, come near and sit down by me. I am overjoyed at the opportunity of profiting for a few moments by the conversation of such a wise woman as you."

"Madame," said the good woman, "I ought not to have such respect shown me, but since you command me, I will obey."

When she had sat down, before they entered into any conversation, one of the Princess' women brought a little low table of mother-of-pearl and ebony, with a china dish full of cakes, and a great many others full of fruits in season and sweetmeats. While they were eating the Princess asked the good woman a great many questions, all of which she answered with modesty. At last the Princess asked her what she thought of the house.

"Madame," answered the devout woman, "I should certainly

have very bad taste to disapprove of anything in it, since it is furnished with remarkably good judgment; yet if you will give me leave to speak my mind freely, I will say that this house would be incomparable if it had three things which are lacking in it."

"My good mother," replied the Princess, "I implore you to tell me what are those things. I will spare no trouble to get them."

"Madame," replied the devout woman, "the first of these three things is the Talking Bird called Bul-bul-ke′zer, which is so singular a creature that it can draw around it all the singing birds of the neighborhood. The second is the Singing Tree, the leaves of which form an harmonious concert of different voices and never cease. The third is the Golden Water, a single drop of which being poured into a vessel increases so as to fill the vessel immediately, and rises up in the middle like a fountain, which continually plays, and yet the basin never overflows."

"Ah! my good mother," cried the Princess, "how much am I obliged to you! I never before heard that there were such curious and wonderful things in the world; but as I am sure you know where they are, do me the favor to tell me."

"Madame," replied the good woman, "I should be unworthy the hospitality you have shown me if I should refuse to satisfy your curiosity on this point, and am glad to tell you that these rarities are all to be met with in the same spot on the confines of this kingdom, towards India. The road lies before your house, and whoever you send needs but follow it for twenty days, and on the twentieth only let him ask the first person he meets where the Talking Bird, the Singing Tree, and the Golden Water are, and he will be informed." After saying this, she rose from her seat, took her leave and went her way.

The Princess Parizade's thoughts were so taken up with the Talking Bird, the Singing Tree, and the Golden Water, that she never perceived the old woman's departure, till she wanted to ask her some further questions. However, she would not send after her visitor, but endeavored to remember all the directions she had given. It seemed to her that she could only be satisfied now if she could get these things into her possession, yet she feared there would be plenty of difficulties and dangers on the way.

She was lost in these thoughts when her brothers returned from hunting, who, when they entered the great hall, instead of finding her lively and gay as she was wont to be, were amazed to see her pensively hanging her head as if something troubled her.

"Sister," said Prince Bahman, "what is become of all your mirth and gaiety? Has some misfortune befallen you? Tell us, that we may know how to act and give you some relief."

The Princess Parizade remained for some time without speaking, but at last she lifted up her eyes to her brothers and said:

"We always thought this house which our late father built for us was so complete that it needed nothing. But this day I have learned that it lacks three things in order to render it the most perfect country seat in the world. These three things are the Talking Bird, the Singing Tree, and the Golden Water." Then she told them all about the visit of the religious woman. "You," she added, "may not think this a matter of great importance, but I am persuaded these rarities are absolutely nec-

essary and I shall not be happy without them. Therefore, whether you value them or not, I desire you to consider what person you may think proper for me to send on this expedition."

"Sister," replied Prince Bahman, "whatever concerns you, concerns us also. It is enough that you have an earnest desire for the things you mention; but even if it were otherwise, we should be anxious to go and search for them on our own account. Only tell me where the place is and I will set out tomorrow."

"Brother," said Prince Perviz, "it is not fitting that you who are the head of the family should be absent so long. I beg you will abandon your design and let me undertake it."

"I am sure of your good will, brother," replied Prince Bahman, "but I have resolved on it and will do it. You shall stay home with our sister and I need not recommend her to your care."

He spent the remainder of that day in making preparations for his journey and in learning from the Princess the directions the devout woman had left her, that he might not miss his way.

Early the next day, Prince Bahman mounted his horse and Prince Perviz and the Princess Parizade embraced him and wished him a pleasant journey. But in the midst of their farewells, it suddenly came over the Princess into what dangers and difficulties she was letting her brother go forth; whereupon she cried out to him, "Ah, brother, I had quite forgotten the difficulties that may lie in the way. Alight, I beseech you, and give up this journey. I would rather never possess the Talking Bird, the Singing Tree and the Golden Water than run the risk of losing you."

"Sister," replied Prince Bahman, "my resolution is fixed and you must allow me to execute it. Nevertheless, as events are uncertain and I may fail, all I can do is to leave you this knife." At that he drew a knife out of his pocket and, presenting it to his sister, said: "Take this knife, sister, and sometimes pull it out of its sheath. While you see it clean as it is now, it shall be a sign that I am alive; but if you find it stained with blood, then you may believe me dead and favor me with your prayers."

The Princess Parizade could obtain nothing more from Prince Bahman. He bade farewell to her and Prince Perviz for the last time, and rode away, well mounted, armed and equipped. When he got into the road, he never turned to the right nor to the left but went straight forward towards India. On the twentieth day he perceived by the roadside a hideous old man, who sat under a tree at some small distance from a thatched house, which was his retreat from the weather. His eyebrows were white as snow, and so was the hair of his head; his whiskers covered his mouth, and his beard and hair reached down to his feet. The nails of his hands and feet were extremely long, and a flat broad hat, like an umbrella, covered his head. He had no clothes but only a mat thrown round his body. This old man was a dervish who had for many years retired from the world, and so neglected himself that at last he had become what we have described.

Prince Bahman stopped when he came near the dervish for here was the first person he had met on the twentieth day.

"God prolong your days, good father, and grant you the fulfilment of your desires," said he.

The dervish returned the Prince's salutation, but so unintelligibly that he could not understand one word he said. Prince Bahman perceived that the reason for this was that the dervish's whiskers hung over his mouth. Being unwilling to go any further without the instruction he wanted, he pulled out a pair of scissors, and having tied his horse to a tree, said: "Good dervish, I want to have a talk with you, but your whiskers prevent my understanding what you say. If you consent, I will cut off part of them, for they disfigure you so much, that you look more like a bear than a man."

The dervish did not oppose the Prince, but let him do it;

and when the Prince had cut off as much hair as he thought fit, he said: "Good dervish, you look now like a man."

The kind behavior of Prince Bahman made the dervish smile. "I am greatly obliged to you," said he, "and am ready to show my gratitude by doing anything in my power for you."

"Good dervish," said Prince Bahman, "I have come a long way and am in search of the Talking Bird, the Singing Tree, and the Golden Water. I beg you to tell me where they may be found, that I may not lose my labor after so long a journey."

While the Prince was speaking, he observed that the dervish changed countenance, looked very serious, and remained silent. At last he said: "I know the way you ask, but the friendship which I feel for you keeps me in suspense as to whether I should tell you what you desire."

"What can hinder you?" asked the prince.

"The danger to which you are going to expose yourself is greater than you believe. A great many brave gentlemen have passed by here and asked me the same question. Though I used all my power to persuade them to desist, they would not believe me. At last I was compelled to show them the way, and I have never seen one come back again. I assure you they have all perished. Therefore, if you have any regard for your life, take my advice. Go no further, but return home."

But Prince Bahman persisted in his resolution. "Whatever the danger," said he, "nothing shall make me change my mind. If any one attacks me, I am well armed, and as brave as any."

"But they who will attack

you are not to be seen," replied the dervish, "and there are a great many of them. How will you defend yourself against foes you cannot see?"

"It is no matter," answered the Prince, "all you say shall not persuade me to do anything contrary to my duty. Since you know the way I beg you once more to tell me."

When the dervish found that he was absolutely bent on pursuing his journey, he put his hand into a bag that lay by him, and pulled out a bowl which he gave to him. "Since I cannot prevail on you to take my advice," said he, "take this bowl. When you are on horse-back throw it before you, and follow it to the foot of a mountain, where it will stop. As soon as it stops, alight, and leave your horse with the bridle thrown over his neck; he will stand in the same place till you return. As you go up the hill, you will see right and left a great quantity of large black stones, and will hear on all sides of you a confusion of voices, which will say a thousand irritating things to discourage you and prevent your climbing to the top of the hill. But take care and be not afraid; and, above all things, do not turn your head to look behind you, for at that instant you will be turned into a black stone like those you see, which are all so many gentlemen who have failed. If you escape the danger of which I give you but a slight description, and get to the top of the mountain, you will see a cage, and in that cage is the Bird you seek. Ask him where are the Singing Tree and Golden Water and he will tell you. I have nothing more to say."

"I am very much obliged to you," said Prince Bahman. "I will endeavor to follow your instructions and not to look behind as I go up and I hope to come and thank you further when I have got what I am in search of." After these words to which the dervish made no answer, he mounted his horse, took leave of the dervish with a low bow, and threw the bowl before him.

The bowl rolled away with such swiftness that Prince Bahman was obliged to spur his horse to follow without losing sight of it. When it came to the foot of the mountain it stopped. The prince alighted and threw the bridle on his horse's neck. Having surveyed the mountain and seen the black stones, the prince began to climb it, but had not gone four steps when he heard the voices mentioned by the dervish, though he could see nobody. Some said, "Where is that fool going? What does he want? Don't let him pass." Others, "Stop him, catch him, kill him," and others with a voice like thunder, "Thief, assassin, murderer!" while some in a gibing tone, cried, "No, no; do not hurt him, let the pretty fellow pass; the cage and bird are kept for him."

Notwithstanding all those troublesome voices, Prince Bahman mounted with courage and resolution for some time, but the voices increased with so loud a din, both in front and behind, that at last he was seized with fear, his legs trembled under him, he staggered, and presently finding that his strength failed, he forgot the dervish's advice, turned about to run down the hill, and was at that instant turned into a black stone as had happened to so many before him. His horse was likewise transformed.

From the time of Prince Bahman's departure, the Princess Parizade always wore the knife and sheath in her girdle, and pulled it out several times a day to know how her brother was faring. For some time she had the consolation of seeing the knife clean and shining. But on the fatal day that Prince Bahman was changed into a stone, the Princess perceived blood running down the point, and was so seized with horror and grief that she threw it down. "Ah, my dear brother," cried she, "why did I ever tell you of the Talking Bird, the Singing Tree, and the Golden Water? Of what importance was it to me to know whether the religious woman thought this house ugly or handsome, complete or not? I wish to heaven I had never seen her."

Prince Perviz was as much afflicted at what had occurred to Prince Bahman as the Princess, but not to waste time in needless regret, he said: "Sister, our regret for our brother is vain. It ought not to prevent us from pursuing our object. I offered to go on this journey. His example has no effect on my resolution. Tomorrow I will go myself."

The Princess did all she could to dissuade Prince Perviz, but all she could urge had no effect upon him. Before he went, that she might know what success he had, he left her a string of a hundred pearls, telling her that if they would not run when she told them upon the string, but remained fixed, that would be a certain sign that he had met the same fate as his brother.

Prince Perviz on the twentieth day from the setting out, met with the dervish. After he had saluted him, he asked if he could tell him where he should find the Talking Bird, the Singing Tree, and the Golden Water. The dervish remonstrated as before, but he could not persuade the Prince to give up his resolution. At last, therefore, he took a bowl out of his bag and gave it to the young man, with the same directions as he had given Prince Bahman, warning him never to turn around at the voices but to continue his way up the hill.

Prince Perviz thanked the dervish and when he had taken leave, he threw the bowl before his horse and followed it. When the bowl came to the bottom of the hill, it stopped and the Prince got off his horse. He encouraged himself, and began to walk up with a resolution to reach the top; but before he had gone six steps, he heard a voice, which seemed to be that of a man behind him, saying in an insulting tone, "Stay, rash youth, that I may punish you for your boldness."

At this affront, the Prince forgot the dervish's advice, clapped his hand upon his sword and drew it, and turned about to revenge himself. But scarcely had he time to see that nobody followed him when he and his horse were changed into black stones.

The day that Prince Perviz was changed to stone, the Princess Parizade was pulling over as usual the pearls which he had left her, when all of a sudden she could not stir them, and never doubted that the Prince, her brother, was dead. As she had determined beforehand what to do in case it should so happen, she lost no time in outward show of grief, but, disguising herself in man's apparel, she mounted her horse the next morning, and took the road her brothers had taken before her. The Princess who was used to riding on horseback, supported the fatigue of so long a journey well, and she also met the dervish on the twentieth day. When she came near him, she alighted off her horse, and leading him by the bridle, she went and sat down by the dervish. "Good dervish," she said, "give me leave to rest by you; and do me the favor to tell me if there are somewhere hereabouts a Talking Bird, a Singing Tree, and Golden Water."

"Madame," answered the dervish, "for by your voice I know you to be a woman disguised in man's apparel, I thank you for the honor you do me. I know very well the place where these things you speak of are to be found, but doubtless you have not been told of the difficulties and dangers which must be surmounted in order to obtain them. Take my advice. Go no further; return and do not urge me to contribute to your ruin."

"Good father," said the princess, "I have come a long way and should be sorry to return home without accomplishing my purpose. You talk of difficulties and dangers, but pray tell me wherein these consist, that I may consider and judge whether I can trust my courage and strength to undertake the journey."

Then the dervish repeated to the Princess Parizade what he had said to the Princes Bahman and Perviz. When he had done, the princess replied: "I own the voices you speak of are capable of striking terror into the most undaunted, but as in all enterprises and dangers every one may use contrivances, I desire to know if I may make use of one."

"And what do you intend to do?" asked the dervish.

"To stop my ears with cotton," said the Princess, "that, however loud and terrible the voices may be, they may make less impression upon me."

"Madame," replied the dervish, "of all the persons who have addressed themselves to me to ask the way, I do not know that anyone has made use of the plan you propose. All I know is, they all perished. If you persist, you can make the experiment, but I would advise you not to expose yourself to the danger."

"My good father," replied the princess, "nothing prevents my persisting. I am sure I shall succeed."

The dervish exhorted her again for the last time to consider well what she was doing, but finding her resolute he gave her a bowl. After the Princess had thanked the dervish and taken leave of him, she mounted her horse, threw the bowl before her, and followed it till it stopped at the foot of the mountain.

The Princess alighted, and stopped her ears with cotton wool. After she had well examined the way by which she was to get to the top, she began at a moderate pace and walked up with undaunted courage. She heard the voices in spite of the cotton, and the higher she went, the louder they seemed; but they could not make any impression on her. She heard a great many affronting speeches and jeering very disagreeable to a woman, which she only laughed at. "I mind not," said she to herself, "all that can be said, were it even worse. I shall pursue my way." At last she got so high that she began to perceive the cage and Bird which also tried to frighten her, crying in a thundering voice, notwithstanding the smallness of its size, "Retire, fool, and approach no nearer."

The Princess nevertheless redoubled her haste and by effort gained the summit of the mountain. Running straight to the cage she clapped her hands upon it and cried: "Bird, I have you in spite of yourself, and you shall not escape me."

While the Princess Parizade was pulling the cotton wool out of her ears, the Bird said to her: "Heroic Princess, I would rather be your slave than any other person's in the world since you have obtained me so courageously. From this instant I swear entire submission to all your commands. The time will come when I shall do you a great service. I know who you are though you do not know yourself and some day I will tell you. As a proof of my sincerity now, tell me what you desire at this moment and I will obey you."

"Bird," said the Princess, "I have been told that there is not far off, Golden Water. Before all things, I ask you to tell me where it is." The Bird showed her the place which was close by, and she went and filled a little silver flagon which she had brought with her. Then she returned to the Bird and said: "Bird, this is not enough, I want also the Singing Tree."

"Turn round," said the Bird, "and you will see behind you a wood where you will find this tree." The Princess went into the wood and by the harmonious sounds she heard, soon knew the tree among many others, but it was very large and high. She came back to the bird and said: "Bird, I have found the Singing Tree, but I can neither pull it up by the roots nor carry it."

The Bird replied: "It is not necessary that you should take it up by the roots. Break off a branch and carry it to plant in your garden. It will grow as fine a tree as this you see."

When the Princess Parizade had in her hand all the three things which she had set out to obtain, she said to the Bird: "Bird, all you have done for me as yet is not enough. My two brothers must be among the black stones which I saw as I came up the hill. I wish to take them home with me."

"What you now ask of me is more difficult than all the rest," said the Bird, "yet I will do it for you. Cast your eyes around and see if you do not find a little pitcher."

"I see it already," said the princess.

"Take it then," said he, "and as you go down the hill, spill a little of the water that is in it on every black stone, and that will be the way to find your brothers again."

The Princess Parizade took up the pitcher, and carried with her the cage and the Bird, the flagon of Golden Water and the branch of the Singing Tree. As she went down the hill, she spilt a little of the water on every black stone, which was changed immediately into a man; and as she did not miss one stone, all of the horses also resumed their former shape. She presently recognized Prince Bahman and Prince Perviz, and they ran to embrace her. Prince Bahman and Prince Perviz perceived how greatly they were indebted to the Princess, their sister, as did all the other gentlemen who had collected round.

"Gentlemen," said the Princess, "I rejoice with you for the happiness which has come to you by my means. Let us however stay no longer where we have nothing to detain us; but mount our horses and return to our respective homes."

When the Princes and all the gentlemen had mounted their horses, the Princess Parizade waited for some of them to lead the way. The two Princes waited for the gentlemen, and they again for the Princess, who, finding that none of them would accept the honor, but that it was reserved for her, said: "Gentlemen, I do not deserve the honor you do me, and accept it only because you desire it." So she led the way, and the two Princes and the gentlemen followed her all together.

As soon as the Princess reached home, she placed the cage in the garden just by the hall; and the Bird no sooner began to sing, than he was surrounded by nightingales, chaffinches, larks, linnets, goldfinches, and a great many other birds of the country. As for the branch of the Singing Tree, it was no sooner set in the midst of the garden than it took root, and in a short time became a large tree, the leaves of which gave as harmonious a concert as those of the tree from which it was gathered. For the Golden Water a large basin of beautiful marble was made in the midst of the garden, and when it was finished the Princess poured into it all the water from the flagon. This increased and swelled so much that it soon reached up to the edges of the basin, and afterwards formed in the middle a fountain twenty feet high, which fell again into the basin without running over.

Some days afterwards, when the Princes Bahman and Perviz had resumed their usual diversion of hunting, they chanced to

meet the Sultan of Persia in so narrow a path that they could not turn away nor retreat without being seen. In their surprise they had only time to alight and prostrate themselves before the Sultan, who seeing they were well mounted and dressed as if they belonged to his court, had some curiosity to see their faces. He stopped and commanded them to rise. The

Princes rose up and stood before him with an easy and graceful air, and respectful, modest countenances. The Sultan then asked them who they were and where they lived.

The Princes made him such polished and prudent answers that the Sultan was charmed with them and asked them at once to join him in the hunt. They therefore mounted their horses again and followed the Sultan. They had not gone very far before they saw a great many wild beasts together. Prince Bahman chose a lion and Prince Perviz a bear and the young men pursued them with such vigor that the Sultan was surprised. They came up with their game and darted their javelins with so much skill, that they pierced, the one the lion and the other the bear, through and through. At that the Sultan felt so kindly disposed towards the two that he invited them to pay him a visit, to which Prince Bahman replied: "Your majesty does us an honor we do not deserve and we beg you will excuse us."

The Sultan, who was astonished that the Princes should refuse this token of his favor, pressed them to tell him why they excused themselves. "Sire," said Prince Bahman, "we have a younger sister, with whom we live in such perfect union that we undertake nothing before we consult her, nor she without our advice."

"I commend your brotherly affection," answered the Sultan. "Consult your sister, and give me your answer here tomorrow."

The Princess Parizade was somewhat surprised at the news her brothers brought her. "It was on my account, I know, that you refused the Sultan," said she, "and I am infinitely obliged to you for it. I perceive by this how strong is your love for me, since you would rather be guilty of incivility towards the Sultan than break the bond that unites us to one another. You judged rightly that if you had once gone, you would by degrees have been led to leave me altogether to devote yourselves to him. Nevertheless, do you think it an easy matter to refuse the Sultan what he seems so eagerly to desire? Sultans will be obeyed and it may be dangerous to oppose him. Before we decide on anything, let us consult the Talking Bird. He is wise and has promised to assist us."

The Princess Parizade sent for the Bird and asked him what they should do in their perplexity. The Bird answered: "The Princes, your brothers, must conform to the Sultan's pleasure, and in their turn ask him to come and see your house."

"But, Bird," replied the Princess, "my brothers and I love one another. Will not this step be injurious to our friendship?"

"Not at all," replied the Bird. "It will become stronger."

Next morning the Princes met the Sultan hunting, who asked them if they had spoken to their sister. Prince Bahman made answer: "Sire, your majesty may dispose of us as you please; we are ready to obey you, for our sister has agreed."

Presuming that the Princes possessed minds equal to their courage and bravery, the Sultan longed with impatience to converse with them more at liberty, and made them ride to the palace on each side of him. When the Sultan entered his capital, the eyes of the people who stood in crowds in the streets, were fixed only upon the two Princes, Bahman and Perviz; and they were anxious to know who they were. All agreed in wishing that the Sultan had been blessed with two such Princes and said: "He might have had children just their age if he had been more fortunate."

The first thing the Sultan did when he arrived was to show the Princes over his palace. Afterwards a magnificent repast was served. The Sultan was a clever and learned man, but in whatever way he turned the conversation, they showed so much judgment and discernment, that he was struck with admiration. "Were these my own children," said he to himself, "and I had improved their talents by suitable education, they could not be better informed."

Before they went out of the Sultan's presence that night, Prince Bahman said: "Sire, may we presume to request that your majesty will do us and our sister the favor to pass by our house and rest and refresh yourself the first time you go hunting?"

"Gentlemen," replied the Sultan, "you and your sister are already dear to me. I will call early tomorrow morning."

When the Princes Bahman and Perviz went home, they gave the Princess Parizade an account of what had passed.

"We must think at once of preparing a repast fit for his majesty," said the Princess. "I will consult the Talking Bird. He will tell us perhaps what dishes the Sultan likes best." The Princes approved and after they retired, she consulted the Bird alone.

"Good mistress," replied the Bird, "you have excellent cooks; let them do the best they can. But above all, let them prepare a dish of cucumbers stuffed with pearls, which must be set before the Sultan in the first course."

"Cucumbers with pearls!" cried the Princess in amazement. "Surely, you know not what you say. It is an unheard-of dish."

"Mistress," said the Bird, "do what I say, and be not uneasy. Nothing but good will follow."

As soon as the Princess got into the house she called for the head cook; and after she had given him directions about the entertainment, she bade him prepare a dish of cucumbers stuffed with pearls. The chief cook who had never heard of such a dish started back and showed his thoughts by his looks. The Princess said, "I see you take me to be mad to order such a dish; nevertheless I give you these orders with the utmost sincerity."

Next day the two Princes went to escort the Sultan and when the latter entered the courtyard and alighted at the portico, the Princess Parizade came and threw herself at his feet. The Sultan stooped to pick her up, and, struck with her good person, and noble air, he said: "The brothers are worthy of the sister and she of them; I am not surprised that the brothers would do nothing without their sister's consent."

The Princess then led the Sultan through the various rooms of the house, all of which he considered attentively and admired excessively. At last she opened a door which led into the garden; and the first object which presented itself to the Sultan's view was the Golden Fountain. Surprised at so rare a sight, he asked whence came such wonderful water, where was its source, and by what art it was made to play so high.

"Sire," replied the Princess, "this water has no communication with any spring; the basin is one single stone, so that the water cannot come in at the sides or underneath. It all proceeded from one flagon, which I emptied into the basin."

Then the Princess led him to the spot where the harmonious Tree was planted; and there the Sultan heard a concert that was different from all the concerts he had ever heard in his life. Stopping to see where the musicians were, he could discern nobody far or near.

"My fair one," said he to the Princess, "where are the musicians? Are they underground or invisible in the air?"

"Sire," answered the Princess, smiling. "It is not musicians, but the Tree your Majesty sees which makes this concert."

The Sultan went nearer and was so charmed with the sweet harmony that he would never have been tired of hearing it.

As he went towards the hall he perceived a prodigious number of singing birds in the trees thereabouts, filling the air with their songs and warblings, and asked why there were so many and none on the other trees in the garden. "The reason, Sire," answered the Princess, "is because they all come to accompany the song of the Talking Bird, which your Majesty may perceive in the cage; and if you listen you will hear that his notes are sweeter than those of all the other birds, even the nightingale."

The Sultan went into the hall, and the Princess said to the Bird, "My slave, here is the Sultan; pay your respects to him."

The Bird left off singing that instant and when all the other birds had ceased one after another, he said: "The Sultan is welcome here. Heaven prosper him, and prolong his life."

As the meal was served by the sofa near the window where the Bird was, the Sultan replied: "Bird, I thank you and am overjoyed to find in you the Sultan of Birds."

As soon as the Sultan saw the dish of cucumbers set before him, thinking they were stuffed in the ordinary manner, he reached out his hand and took one; but when he cut it, he was extremely surprised to find it stuffed with pearls. "What is this?" cried he in great astonishment; "why are these cucumbers stuffed with pearls? Pearls are not to be eaten!" But the Bird, interrupting, demanded of him: "Can your Majesty stop and question at such a small matter as cucumbers stuffed with pearls, when you accepted altogether without question the statement that the Sultaness your wife, had passed off a dog, a cat, and a piece of wood as your children?"

"Ah!" replied the Sultan, "I believed it, because the two aunts assured me of it."

"The Sultaness' two sisters," replied the Bird, "were envious of her happiness in being preferred by your Majesty before them, and so they deceived you. If you question them, they will confess their crime. The two brothers and the sister whom you see before you are your own children, whom they sent adrift, and who were taken in and reared by the keeper of your gardens."

This speech of the Bird's illumined the Sultan's understanding. "Bird," cried he, "I believe the truth of what you tell me. Come, then, my children; come, my daughter, let me embrace you." Then he rose up, and having embraced the two Princes and the

Princess and mingled his tears with theirs, he said: "I am persuaded you are such children as will maintain the royal glory of the Sultans of Persia, and am deeply grateful to the keeper of my gardens for the care he has taken of you."

After this, he sat down again and finished his meal, and when he had done, he said, "My children, tomorrow I will bring to you the Sultaness, your mother. Therefore prepare to receive her."

Afterwards the Sultan mounted his horse and returned in great haste to his capital. The first thing he did as soon as he alighted and entered his palace, was to command the grand vizier to try the Sultaness' two sisters. They were taken from their homes separately, convicted, and condemned to be executed; which sentence was carried out within the hour.

In the meantime, the Sultan, followed by all the lords of his court, went to fetch the Sultaness out of the miserable confinement in which she had languished, and embracing her, he said with tears in his eyes: "I come, madame, to ask your pardon for the injustice I have done you, and to make you the reparation I ought. I have begun by punishing the unnatural wretches who put this abominable cheat upon me; and I hope you will look upon it as complete when I present to you two accomplished Princes and a charming lovely Princess, our children. Come and resume your former rank and all the honors which are your due." All this was done and said before great crowds of people who immediately spread the news through the town.

Early the next morning, the Sultan and Sultaness went with all their court to the house built by the keeper, where the sultan presented the Princes Bahman and Perviz, and the Princess Parizade to the Sultaness. "These, madame," said he, "are the two Princes, your sons, and the Princess, your daughter; embrace them with the same tenderness that I have done, since they are worthy both of you and of me." The tears flowed plentifully down their cheeks at these tender embraces, especially the Sultaness', so great was the comfort and joy of having two such Princes for her sons, and such a Princess for her daughter, on whose account she had endured affliction so long.

The two Princes and the Princess had prepared a magnificent repast for the Sultan and Sultaness and their court. As soon as that was over the Sultan led the Sultaness into the garden and showed her the Singing Tree and the Golden Fountain. As for the Bird she had already seen and admired him in his cage.

When there was nothing to detain the Sultan any longer, he took horse again, and with the Princes Bahman and Perviz on his right hand, and the Sultaness and the Princess at his left, surrounded by all the officers of his court, he returned to his capital. Crowds of people came out to meet them, and with acclamations of joy ushered them into the city, where all eyes were fixed, not only on the Sultaness, the two Princes, and the Princess, but also upon the Bird which the Princess carried before her in his cage. He was singing the sweet notes that drew all the other birds after him, flying from tree to tree in the country, and from one house-top to another in the city. The Princes Bahman and Perviz and the Princess Parizade were at length brought to the palace, and nothing was heard or seen all that night and for many days thereafter but illuminations and rejoicings both in the palace and in the utmost parts of the city.

Painting from the Collection of the John Hancock Mutual Life Ins. Co.

A WHALING ADVENTURE

For real adventure nothing could equal whaling in the old days of sailing ships. As soon as a whale was sighted, men left the ship in a little row-boat, not over eighteen feet long, to attack a whale at least sixty feet long and weighing fifty tons. And the great sperm whale was a fighter. It would attack pursuers both with its huge, gaping mouth and with its enormous tail. Sometimes it bit a small boat in two or smashed it to pieces with a single stroke of its tail.

One morning some men set out from their ship in a small boat to get a whale. Trying to avoid its terrible mouth and tail, they rowed close up to its middle until they were near enough to use a harpoon. Then the man standing in the bow of the boat slung his harpoon with full force, embedding the barbed iron point deep in the back of the whale. And at the feel of that barb, the maddened whale dashed away, dragging the small boat after it by the long rope which was attached to the harpoon. Fairly leaping out of the water, that little cockleshell of a boat went surging after the great sea monster.

And now a battle royal was on, for as the whale perceived that it could not shake off its pursuers, it turned and made fiercely for them. Lifting its head, it rose until it seemed to be standing almost erect in the water. Bearing down on the side of the boat, it so nearly rolled her over that some of the men were thrown, screaming, into the sea. Then one of the sailors drove an oar into its yawning jaws and it fell back, baffled, so the boat righted itself, and the men in the water scrambled back aboard her. But the whale remained baffled for a moment only. In another instant it dove and came up under the boat. Using its nose, it struck her terrific blows from below, tossing her bow in the air. Again she almost capsized. Then the whale darted forth. Scourging the water with its tail, it went dashing off for a second time. Thrashing round and round in circles in a frantic attempt to free itself from the harpoon, it dragged the small boat round and round in circles with it.

On and on that whale struggled until it was completely exhausted and could be finished with a knife. Then the men towed it back to the ship where they were greeted with cheers by the sailors who had been watching the battle.

At that time all the oil for lamps to light homes and city streets came from whales. But catching whales was a business for only the boldest, most daring men.

The Enchanted Island*

HOWARD PYLE

Once upon a long, long time ago, and in a country far, far away, there lived two men in the same town and both were named Selim; one was Selim the Baker, and one was Selim the Fisherman.

Selim the Baker was well off in the world, but Selim the Fisherman was only so-so. Selim the Baker always had plenty to eat and a warm corner in cold weather, but many and many a time Selim the Fisherman's stomach went empty and his teeth went chattering.

Once it happened that for time after time Selim the Fisherman caught nothing but bad luck in his nets, and not so much as a single sprat, and he was very hungry. "Come," said he to himself, "those who have some should surely give to those who have none," and so he went to Selim the Baker. "Let me have a loaf of bread," said he, "and I will pay you for it tomorrow."

"Very well," said Selim the Baker; "I will let you have a loaf if you will give me all that you catch in your nets tomorrow."

"So be it," said Selim the Fisherman.

So the next day Selim the Fisherman fished and fished and fished and fished, and still he caught no more than the day before; until just at sunset he cast his net for the last time for the day, and, lo and behold! there was something heavy in it. So he dragged it ashore, and what should it be but a leaden box, sealed as tight as wax, and covered with all manner of strange letters and figures. "Here," said he, "is something to pay for my bread of yesterday, at any rate;" and off he marched to Selim the Baker.

They opened the box in the baker's shop, and within they found two rolls of yellow linen. In each of the rolls of linen was another little leaden box; in one was a finger-ring of gold set

*Taken from *Twilight Land*. Used by permission of the publishers. Harper & Brothers.

with a red stone, in the other was a finger-ring of iron set with nothing at all. That was all the box held; nevertheless, that was the greatest catch that ever any fisherman made in the world; for, though Selim the one or Selim the other knew no more of the matter than the cat under the stove, the gold ring was the Ring of Luck and the iron ring was the Ring of Wisdom.

Inside the gold ring were carved these letters: "Whosoever wears me, shall have that which all men seek—for so it is with good-luck in this world." Inside the iron ring were written these words: "Whosoever wears me, shall have that which few men care for—and that is the way it is with wisdom in our town."

"Well," said Selim the Baker, and he slipped the gold ring of good-luck on his finger, "I have driven a good bargain, and you have paid for your loaf of bread."

"But what will you do with the other ring?" said Selim the Fisherman.

"Oh, you may have that," said Selim the Baker.

Well, that evening, as Selim the Baker sat in front of his shop in the twilight smoking a pipe of tobacco, the ring he wore began to work. Up came a little old man with a white beard, and he was dressed all in gray from top to toe, and he wore a black velvet cap, and he carried a long staff in his hand. He stopped in front of Selim the Baker, and stood looking at him a long, long time. At last—"Is your name Selim?" said he.

"Yes," said Selim the Baker, "it is."

"And do you wear a gold ring with a red stone on your finger?"

"Yes," said Selim, "I do."

"Then come with me," said the little old man, "and I will show you the wonder of the world."

"Well," said Selim the Baker, "that will be worth the seeing, at any rate." So he emptied out his pipe of tobacco, and put on his hat and followed the way the old man led.

Up one street they went, and down another, through alleys and byways where Selim had never been before. At last they came to where a high wall ran along the narrow street, with a garden behind it, and by-and-by to an iron gate. The old man rapped upon the gate three times with his knuckles, and cried in a loud voice, "Open to Selim, who wears the Ring of Luck!" Then instantly the gate swung open, and Selim the Baker followed the old man into the garden.

Bang! shut the gate behind him, and there he was.

There he was! And such a place he had never seen before. Such fruit! such flowers! such fountains! such summer-houses!

"This is nothing," said the old man; "this is only the beginning of wonder. Come with me."

He led the way down a long pathway between the trees. By-and-by, far away, they saw the light of torches; and when they came to what they saw, lo and behold! there was the seashore, and a boat with four-and-twenty oarsmen, each dressed in cloth of gold and silver more splendidly than a prince. And there were four-and-twenty black slaves, carrying each a torch of spicewood, so that all the air was filled with sweet smells. The old man led the way, and Selim, following, entered the boat; and there was a seat for him made soft with satin cushions embroidered with gold. Selim wondered whether he was not dreaming.

The oarsmen pushed off from the shore and away they rowed. On they rowed and on they rowed for all that livelong night.

At last morning broke, and then as the sun rose, Selim saw such a sight as never mortal eyes beheld before or since. It was the wonder of wonders—a great city built on an island. The island was all one mountain; and on it, one above another and another above that again, stood palaces that glistened like snow, and orchards of fruits, and gardens of flowers and green trees.

And as the boat came nearer and nearer to the city, Selim could see that all around on the house-tops and down to the water's edge were crowds and crowds of people. All were looking out towards the sea, and when they saw the boat and Selim in it, a great shout went up like the roaring of rushing waters.

"It is the King! It is the King! It is Selim the King!"

Then the boat landed, and there stood scores of princes and nobles to welcome Selim ashore. And there was a white horse waiting for him to ride, and its saddle and bridle were studded with diamonds and rubies and emeralds that sparkled and glistened like the stars in heaven, and Selim thought for sure he must be dreaming with his eyes open.

Up the hill he rode, and to the grandest and most splendid of all the splendid palaces, the princes and noblemen with him, and the crowd shouting as though to split their throats, And

what a palace it was!—as white as snow and painted all inside with gold and blue. All around it were gardens blooming. There they made a king of Selim, and put a golden crown on his head; and that is what the Ring of Good Luck can do for a baker. But wait a bit! There was something queer about it all!

All that day was feasting and drinking and merry-making, and the twinging and twanging of music, and dancing of beautiful dancing-girls. And when night came they lit thousands and thousands of candles of perfumed wax. But at last it came midnight, and then suddenly, in an instant, all the lights went out and everything was dark as pitch—not a spark, not a glimmer anywhere. And, just as suddenly, all the sounds of music and dancing and merry-making ceased, and everybody began to wail and cry until it was enough to wring one's heart to hear. Then, in the midst of all the wailing and crying, a door was flung open, and in came six tall and terrible black men, dressed all in white from top to toe, carrying each a flaming torch; and by the light of the torches King Selim saw that all—princes, noblemen, dancing-girls—all lay on their faces on the floor.

The six men took King Selim—who shuddered and shook with fear—by the arms, and marched him through dark, gloomy entries and passageways, until they came at last to the very heart of the palace.

There was a great high-vaulted room of black marble, and in the middle of it a pedestal with seven steps, all of black marble; and on the pedestal stood a stone statue of a woman looking as natural as life, only that her eyes were shut. The statue was dressed like a queen; she wore a golden crown on her head; and upon her body hung golden robes, set with diamonds and emeralds and rubies and sapphires and pearls. As for the face of the statue, ink could not tell how beautiful it was. When Selim looked at it, it made his heart stand still in his breast.

The six men brought Selim up in front of the statue, and then a voice came as though from the vaulted roof: "Selim! Selim! Selim!" it said, "what art thou doing? Today is feasting and drinking and merry-making, but beware of tomorrow!"

As soon as these words were ended the six black men marched King Selim back whence they had brought him; there they left him and passed out one by one as they had first come in, and the door shut to behind them.

Then in an instant the lights flashed on again, the music began to play and the people began to talk and laugh, and King Selim thought that maybe all that had just passed was only a bit of an ugly dream after all.

So that is the way King Selim the Baker began to reign. All day was feasting and drinking and making merry and music and laughing and talking. But every night at midnight the same thing happened, the lights went out, all the people began wailing and crying, and the six tall, terrible black men came with fantastic torches and marched King Selim away to the beautiful statue. And every night the same voice said—"Selim! Selim! Selim! What art thou doing? Today is feasting and drinking and merry-making; but beware of tomorrow!"

So things went on for a twelve-month, and at last came the end of the year. That day and night the merry-making was wilder and madder then it had ever been before, but the great clock in the tower went on—tick, tock! tick, tock!—and by-and-by it came midnight. Then, as it always happened, the lights went out, and all was as black as ink. But this time there was no wailing and crying out; everything was silent as death; the door opened slowly, and in came, not six black men as before, but nine men as silent as death, dressed all in flaming red, and the torches they carried burned as red as blood. They took King Selim by the arms, just as the six men had done, and marched him through the passageways, to the same vaulted room. There stood the statue, but now it was turned to flesh and blood, and the eyes were open and looking straight at Selim the Baker.

"Art thou Selim?" said she; and she pointed her finger at him.

"Yes, I am Selim," said he.

"And dost thou wear the gold ring with the red stone?"

"Yes," said he; "I have it on my finger."

"And dost thou wear the iron ring?"

"No," said he; "I gave that to Selim the Fisherman."

The words had hardly left his lips when the statue gave a great cry and clapped her hands together. In an instant an echoing cry sounded all over the town—a shriek fit to split the ears.

The next moment there came another sound—a sound like thunder—above and below and everywhere. The earth began to shake and to rock, and the houses began to topple and fall, and the people began to scream and to yell and to shout, and the waters of the sea began to lash and to roar, and the wind began to bellow and howl. Then it was a good thing for King Selim that he wore Luck's Ring; for, though all the beautiful snow-white palace about him and above him began to crumble to pieces like slaked lime, the sticks and the stones and the beams to fall this side of him and that, he crawled out from under it without a scratch or a bruise, like a rat out of a cellar.

That is what Luck's Ring did for him. But his troubles were

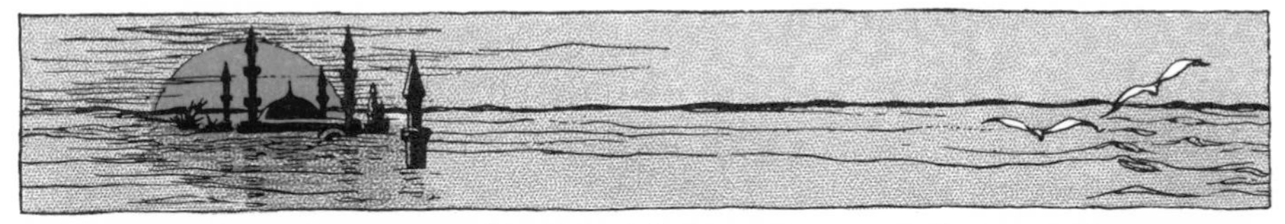

not over yet; for now the island began to sink into the water, carrying everything with it except an empty boat. King Selim quickly jumped into it to save himself from drowning.

The boat floated on until it came to another island. Only on this island there was no blade of grass nor living thing of any kind. There Selim went ashore, and there he would have starved only for Luck's Ring. One day men sailing by in a boat heard poor Selim's shouts and came and took him aboard. How they all stared to see his golden crown and his jewels!

Before they would consent to carry him away, they made him give up all the fine things he had. Then they took him home again, just as poor as when he had started. Back he went to his bake-shop and the first thing he did was to take off his gold ring and put it on the shelf.

"If this is the Ring of Good Luck," said he, "I do not want to wear the like of it."

And now for Selim the Fisherman. Well, thus it happened to him. For a while he carried the iron ring around in his pocket. But one day he slipped it on his finger. After that he never took it off again, and the world went smoothly with him. He was not rich, but then he was not poor; for I never yet knew wisdom to go begging or crying. He went his way and he fished his fish. Then one day he went past the baker shop and there sat Selim the Baker smoking his pipe.

"So, friend," said Selim the Fisherman, "you are back again!"

"Yes," said the other Selim, "awhile ago I was a king, and now I am nothing but a baker again. As for that Luck's Ring, when next I wear it may I be hanged!"

Thereupon he told Selim the Fisherman the story of what

had happened with the Ring of Good Luck.

"Well!" said Selim the Fisherman, "I should like to have a sight of that island myself. If you want the ring no longer, just let me have it!"

"You may have it," said Selim the Baker. "And you are welcome to it." So Selim the Fisherman put on the ring.

That night, as he came home carrying his nets over his shoulder, whom should he meet but the little old man in gray.

"Is your name Selim?" said the little man, just as he had before.

"Yes," said Selim, "it is."

"And do you wear a gold ring with a red stone?"

"Yes," said Selim, "I do."

"Then come with me," said the little old man, "and I will show you the wonder of the world."

Selim the Fisherman dropped his nets and went after the other Selim as fast as his legs would carry him until they reached the garden to which Selim the Baker had been brought.

To make a long story short, everything happened to Selim the Fisherman just as it had happened to Selim the Baker. At dawn of the day they came to the island and the city built on the mountain. And the palaces were just as white and beautiful, and the gardens and orchards just as fresh and blooming as though they had not all tumbled down and sunk under the water a week before. There Selim the Fisherman was greeted with great pomp, and they made a king of him, just as they had made a king of Selim the Baker.

That night, as the hour of midnight struck, the same six terrible black men with torches led Selim the Fisherman to the same vaulted room with the same beautiful statue.

Then came the voice from above—"Selim! Selim! Selim! what art thou doing? Today is feasting and drinking and merry-making but beware of tomorrow!"

But Selim the Fisherman did not stand still and listen, as Selim the Baker had done. He had listened well to the story of Selim the Baker and had learned from it.

He called out, "I hear the words! I am listening! I will beware today for the sake of tomorrow!"

First of all he called the wisest men of the island to him, and found from them just where the other desert island lay upon which the boat with Selim the Baker had drifted.

Then he sent armies of men and built on that island palaces and houses, and planted there orchards and gardens, just like the ones about him—only a great deal finer. Then he sent fleets of ships and carried everything away from the island where he lived to that other island. At last he sent over the beautiful statue and had it set up in his palace. Then he went over himself, leaving nothing behind him. So came midnight at the end of twelve months. Everything was silent as death. Again the same nine men came with torches burning. They took Selim the Fisherman and led him to the beautiful statue, and there she was with her eyes open.

"Are you Selim?" said she.

"Yes I am Selim," said he.

"And do you wear the iron Ring of Wisdom?" said she.

"Yes, I do," said he, and so he did.

There was no roaring and thundering, for this island was solid rock and not all enchantment and hollow inside like the other. The beautiful statue smiled. She came down from the pedestal where she stood and kissed Selim the Fisherman on the lips.

"I have done all this for you!" said Selim the Fisherman.

"And I have been waiting for you a thousand years!" said the beautiful statue—only she was not a statue any longer.

After that they were married, and Selim the Fisherman and the enchanted statue became king and queen in real earnest.

So, after all, it is not always the lucky one who gathers the plums when wisdom is by to pick up what the other shakes down.

These illustrations are from the original ones by Howard Pyle, the greatest illustrator America has produced. Born in 1853, he became particularly interested in American history. See his *Book of Pirates* and *Robin Hood*.

The Circus Man*

PHINEAS T. BARNUM (*American*, 1810–1891)

ON ANY day of the week in 1819 or thereabouts, a certain barefoot boy might have been seen about the quiet town of Bethel, Connecticut. While he was helping on his parents' farm or doing errands in the town young Phineas Barnum was always figuring out how to make a little extra money. Money was scarce at home, and the boy delighted in his money-making schemes. On holidays, when his playmates were busy spending the pennies that they had saved, Phineas was just as busy planning how to part them from these hard-won riches. He usually managed to do this by finding just the right thing to sell. He had already learned what people wanted to spend their money on and how to make a shrewd but fair bargain.

When Phineas was twenty-five, he had settled down to running a country store. One day he heard the interesting tale of Joice Heth. This unusual Negro woman was said to be one hundred sixty-one years old, and also, the nurse of George Washington. How thrilled people would be to see her, to be able to tell their friends that they had met the old woman who was supposed to have taken care of George Washington as a baby!

Barnum was filled with excitement. This was the kind of business for him! He sold his store for five hundred dollars and used most of the money to attract public interest in seeing Joice Heth. He wrote such advertisements for the newspapers that in

*This story is told from Barnum's own autobiography which is not only an interesting story of a picturesque life, but a fascinating history of the development of the American circus by the greatest showman in America.

every big city he visited, crowds were waiting to pay to see her. He earned a vast return on his money.

When the old woman died, Phineas Barnum looked about for another person of such attraction that they could both make money and please the throngs which waited to be entertained. Signor Vivalla was such a man. He was an Italian juggler who could spin plates, perform remarkable balancing feats and walk on stilts, things that most people had never before seen. Again, Barnum made use of his sensational advertising skill and Vivalla became most popular.

But now another lesson in showmanship was to be learned. One evening when Vivalla made his appearance, a member of the audience began to hiss and boo. Curious, Barnum questioned the troublemaker and discovered that this fellow felt that he could do everything that Vivalla could, but just a bit better! Here was an opportunity to turn a problem into an advantage.

Barnum immediately challenged the troublemaker to compete in a series of public contests to prove which one was the better juggler. Wide advertising brought great public interest, and in the end Barnum and both performers made more money than ever.

In April, 1839, Barnum and Vivalla joined Aaron Turner's Traveling Circus Company. Barnum was to act as ticket seller, secretary, and treasurer. Traveling from town to town and performing in canvas tents was altogether a new experience for Barnum, although the idea of circuses in one form or another had begun in England about King Arthur's time.

In time Barnum began to long for a more settled form of show business. The American Museum in New York City was for sale. This unusual museum housed the most interesting collection of curiosities Barnum had ever seen. He bought it and, as its new owner, was able to present to the public an interesting and exciting show. In his new circus were many rare beasts and remarkably trained animals, even performing fleas, seen with their tiny carriages and outfits through a magnifying glass. Barnum presented giants, dwarfs, jugglers, ventriloquists, tightrope dancers, gypsies, and remarkable mechanical figures.

He had such a remarkable understanding of human nature, so keen and merry a wit, that he was always able to startle public attention and keep people thinking and talking about his performances. And not only could he use his wit to attract people into the Museum, he could also use it to get them out again. Sometimes visitors would bring their luncheons and stay all day in the building, so crowding it that other would-be visitors had to be turned away and their twenty-five-cent admission fee was lost. Once, on St. Patrick's Day, a crowd of Irish people thronged the place giving every evidence of intending to stay until sundown. Beholding an eager crowd without, pressing to get in, and the ticket-seller forced of necessity to refuse their quarters, Barnum attempted to induce one Irish lady with two children to leave the place by politely showing her an egress, or way out of the building, through a back door into a sidestreet. But the lady haughtily remarked that she had her dinner and intended to stay all day. Desperate by this time, Barnum ordered a sign painter to paint on a large sign the words

TO THE EGRESS

This sign he placed over the steps leading to the backdoor where the crowd must see it after they had once been around the whole building and seen all there was to see. Plunging down the stairs, they read TO THE EGRESS and, not knowing the meaning of the word, doubtless thinking it sounded a good deal like Tigress, they shouted aloud, "Sure that's some new kind of animal!"

Eager to take in everything, they crowded out the door only to find that this wonderful new curiosity was the back street!

Once Barnum engaged a band of wild Indians from Iowa, for the Museum. The party consisted of a number of large, noble savages; beautiful squaws; and interesting papooses. The men gave war dances on the stage with a vigor and enthusiasm that delighted the audiences. Nevertheless, these wild Indians con-

sidered their dances as realities and it was dangerous to get in their way. Indeed, a rope fence had to be built at the front of the stage to make certain that they would not plunge down upon their audience after one of their rousing war dances.

Finding the responsibility of thus protecting the public to be rather heavy, Mr. Barnum decided to ask them to change their bill by giving a wedding dance instead of a war dance. But the Indians took a wedding dance as seriously as they had the war dance. At the first performance, Mr. Barnum was informed that he was expected to provide a large, new, red woolen blanket at a cost of ten dollars for the bridegroom to present to the father of the bride. He ordered the purchase made, but was considerably taken aback when he was told that he must have another new blanket for the evening's performance, as the old chief would not permit his daughter to be approached with the wedding dance unless he had his blanket as a present. Barnum explained that this was not a real wedding, but the old savage gave such a terrific "Ugh!" that Barnum was glad to make his peace by ordering another blanket. He was out $120.00 for twelve wedding blankets that week!

Among the giants he exhibited, Mr. Barnum had Monsieur Bihin, a Frenchman; and the Arabian, Colonel Goshen. One day the two giants had a terrific quarrel. Running to the collection of arms in the Museum, one seized the club with which Captain

Painting from the Collection of the John Hancock Mutual Life Ins. Co.

The Greatest Show on Earth

Step right up, ladies and gents!
This way to excitement and mirth.
The one, the only—Barnum's Circus,
The Greatest Show on Earth!

Cook was said to have been killed and the other snatched up a crusader's sword of tremendous size and weight. Everything seemed ready for hopeless tragedy, but once again Barnum's quick and ready wit saved the day. Rushing in between the two raging combatants, he cried: "Look here! You are under engagement to me, and if the duel is to come off, I and the public have a right to participate. It must be duly advertised and must take place on our stage. No performance of yours would be a greater attraction!" This proposition, apparently made with such earnestness, caused the two huge creatures to burst into laughter after which they shook hands and quarreled no more.

Barnum's success as a showman made him very rich, but nothing he did in his life gave him greater satisfaction than his bringing to the United States, the sweet singer, Jenny Lind, who was called the Swedish Nightingale.

In an elaborate home at Bridgeport, Connecticut, Barnum lived for many years, frequently making generous gifts to benefit the town. One great fortune he lost through an ill-advised business deal, but he wasted no time in regrets. Immediately he set about making another fortune. His little friend, Tom Thumb, came to him at that time and generously offered to help him. So Barnum took Tom Thumb to Europe and exhibited him there, sending every penny he could back home to pay his debts. Thus he paid all his obligations and found himself once again in possession of his beloved American Museum.

Twice that museum was destroyed by fire, but nothing discouraged Barnum. He built it up anew. He now determined to devote himself entirely to a great traveling circus, far larger and better than anything that had ever been done before. On this circus he labored unremittingly confident that, if he devoted his best energies to the public, the public would liberally repay him. Perceiving that his show was too gigantic to be moved in the old way by wagons, he now for the first time arranged with railroads to transport it, using seventy freight cars, six passenger cars, and three engines. The circus was a tremendous success. People crowded to the various places of exhibition, coming not only from the towns where the show was held, but from neighboring towns as well, some on excursion trains and some by wagons or on horseback, often camping out over night.

Two years later, on the day before Christmas, Barnum was sitting at breakfast in a hotel, thinking comfortably how he had arranged for his circus to be shown in New York in order that his vast host of men should not be thrown out of employment during the winter, when once again a telegram was handed him saying that a fire had completely destroyed his circus. This time Barnum had no thought of giving up again.

"There need be," said he, "no real misfortunes since even that which seems an overwhelming misfortune can be turned into an opportunity for rising to greater accomplishments."

Therefore, he merely interrupted his breakfast long enough on this occasion to go out and send immediate cables to his European agents to duplicate all his animals within two months. He then went back and finished his meal.

By the first of April, he placed on the road a combination of curiosities and marvels far surpassing anything that he had ever done before.

But great as this circus was, Barnum was never satisfied to rest on his laurels. He aimed to do something still greater. In 1874, while he still continued the traveling circus, he opened a great Roman Hippodrome in New York. This gorgeous spectacle began every evening with a Congress of Nations—a grand procession of gilded chariots and triumphal cars, conveying Kings, Queens and Emperors, each surrounded by his respective retinue, and all in costumes made with the greatest care to be historically correct. This vast pageant contained nearly one-thousand persons and several hundred horses besides elephants, camels,

llamas, ostriches, elands, zebras, and reindeer. The rich and varied costumes, armor and trappings, gorgeous banners and paraphernalia, as well as the appropriate music accompanying the entrance of each nation, produced an effect brilliant and bewildering. The entire press said that never before, since the days of the Caesars, had there been so grand a public spectacle.

In 1880, Barnum took James A. Bailey into partnership with him in the traveling-circus business. This partnership with Bailey lasted throughout the remainder of Barnum's life. They opened their combined show with a street parade by night in New York, all beautifully illuminated by calcium lights.

This huge circus now had its own cars when it traveled. Advance agents and advertising cars—gorgeous with paint and gilding, containing paste vats, posters and a force of men—would pass through the country weeks ahead of the circus, pasting up the billboards and arousing the interest of the community. The circus, itself, was packed up in the smallest possible space, its men trained with military precision to work like clockwork and make every move count in erecting or taking down the huge canvas city. The performers slept in their cars and ate in the canvas dining-tent. Hundreds of men were employed and the expenses of the concern were four- or five-thousand dollars a day. Thus far had circuses grown since Barnum's early days.

One of the most interesting feats of Barnum's later years was the purchase of Jumbo, the largest elephant ever seen. Jumbo was the chief ornament of the Zoological Gardens in London, and a great favorite with English children. When Barnum's agents tried to remove Jumbo, Alice, another elephant who had been Jumbo's companion, grew so excited that her groans and trumpetings frightened all the other beasts in the Zoo so that they set up such howlings and roarings as to be heard a mile away. Midst such a grievous farewell, Jumbo was led forth into the street. When he found himself in such unfamiliar surroundings, he lay down on the pavement and would not budge. In dismay Barnum's agent cabled him: "Jumbo has laid down in the street and won't get up. What shall we do?"

Barnum immediately replied: "Let him lie there a week if he wants to. It is the best advertisement in the world."

Finally, Jumbo in his cage was dragged by twenty horses to a waiting steamer where quarters had been prepared by cutting away one of the decks. Thus he was brought to America, and, later, Barnum acquired Alice as well.

In 1884, Barnum got the rarest specimen of all his zoo, a sacred white elephant from Burma. The animal came to America in all his gorgeous trappings, accompanied by a Burmese orchestra and a retinue of Buddhist priests in full ecclesiastical costume.

Mr. Barnum built for his great show enormous winter quarters at Bridgeport. A ten-acre lot was enclosed and, in this enclosure, numerous buildings were constructed. There was an elephant house, kept heated at just the right temperature naturally required by these animals, where thirty or forty elephants could be luxuriously housed and trained. Another building held lions, tigers, and leopards, which require a different temperature; and still another housed camels and caged animals. The monkeys had roomy quarters all to themselves where they could roam about and work their mischievous will unrestrained. The hippopotami and sea-lions had a huge pond heated by steam pipes, and here the elephants also were permitted their supreme enjoyment, a bath. There was a nursery department for the receipt and care of new-born animals; and, in the various buildings, many of the beasts were permitted to leave their cages and frolic at large.

Four times during his career, great fires nearly wiped Barnum out and, in 1887, his wife awoke him in the middle of the night to tell him that a fifth great fire had destroyed his splendid winter quarters at Bridgeport.

"I am very sorry, my dear," he said calmly, "but apparent evils are often blessings in disguise." And with that, he was once again fast asleep!

Barnum was now seventy-seven years old; but, with the help of his partner, Mr. Bailey, he rose as triumphant from this last fire as from all the others and soon had a better circus than ever. His energy, pluck, and ambition gave the people a better, cleaner, and more complete performance than has ever been given by any other showman. With his kindly face beaming, he often said: "To me there is no picture so beautiful as ten-thousand smiling, bright-eyed, happy children; no music so sweet as their clear, ringing laughter. That I have had power, by providing innocent amusement for the little ones, to create such pictures to evoke such music is my proudest and happiest reflection."

THE ADVENTURES OF GENERAL TOM THUMB

A TRUE STORY

Told by the World-Renowned Show-Man

PHINEAS T. BARNUM

who, as proprietor of the American Museum in New York, discovered in the year 1842 a veritable

TOM THUMB

the most famous little man ever known to the world. He visited the Courts of

KINGS AND QUEENS

captivated the hearts of the multitude, and proved ever so merry, quick-witted and bright that he furnished to all the same innocent pleasure and mirth as the fabled Tom Thumb of our stories

IN November, 1842, I (Phineas T. Barnum)* heard of a remarkably small child, and at my request, my brother brought him to my hotel. He was not two feet high, weighed less than sixteen pounds, and was the smallest child I ever saw that could walk alone. He was a perfectly formed, bright-eyed little fellow, with light hair and ruddy cheeks, and he enjoyed the best of health. He was exceedingly bashful but, after some coaxing, he was induced to talk with me, and he told me that he was the son of Sherwood E. Stratton and that his own name was Charles E. Stratton. After seeing and talking with him, I at once determined to secure his services from his parents and to exhibit him in public. He and his mother came to New York Thanksgiving Day, 1842, and I announced him at once on my Museum bills as "General Tom Thumb."

I took the greatest pains to educate and train my diminutive prodigy, devoting many hours to the task by day and night, and I was very successful, for he was an apt pupil, with a great deal of native talent, and a keen sense of the ludicrous. He speedily became a public favorite. Accordingly I entered into an agreement for his services for another year with the privilege of exhibiting him in Europe.

*Arranged from *The Life of P. T. Barnum*, written by himself.

On January 18, 1844, I went on board the new and fine sailing ship, *Yorkshire*, bound for Liverpool. Our party included General Tom Thumb, his parents, and his tutor. We were accompanied by several personal friends, and the City Brass Band kindly volunteered to escort us to Sandy Hook.

On our arrival at Liverpool, quite a crowd had assembled at the dock to see Tom Thumb, for it had been previously announced that he would arrive on the *Yorkshire*, but his mother managed to smuggle him ashore unnoticed, for she carried him, as if he were an infant, in her arms.

Immediately after our arrival in London, the General came out at the Princess's Theatre, and made so decided a "hit" that it was difficult to decide who was best pleased, the spectators, the manager, or myself. I took a furnished mansion in West End in the very centre of the most fashionable locality. From this magnificent mansion I sent letters of invitation to the editors and several of the nobility to visit the General. Most of them called and were highly gratified. The word of approval was indeed so passed around in high circles, that uninvited parties drove to my door in crested carriages and were not admitted.

During our first week in London, the Hon. Edward Everett, the American minister, to whom I had letters of introduction, called and was highly pleased with his diminutive, though renowned countryman. We dined with him the next day, by invitation, and his family loaded the young American with presents. Mr. Everett kindly promised to use his influence at the palace with a view of having Tom Thumb introduced to Her Majesty Queen Victoria. I breakfasted at his house one morning in company with Mr. Charles Murray, who held the office of Master of the Queen's Household. Mr. Murray kindly offered his good offices in the case, and the next day one of the Queen's Life Guards, a tall, noble-looking fellow, bedecked as became his station, brought me a note, conveying the Queen's invitation to General Tom Thumb and his guardian, Mr. Barnum, to appear at Buckingham Palace on an evening specified. Special instructions were the same day given me by Mr. Murray, by Her Majesty's command, to suffer the General to appear before her as he would appear anywhere else, without any training in the use of the titles of royalty, as the Queen desired to see him act naturally and without restraint.

On arriving at the Palace, the Lord in Waiting put me under drill as to the manner and form in which I should conduct myself in the presence of royalty. I was to answer all questions by Her Majesty through him, and, in no event, to speak directly to the

Queen. In leaving the royal presence, I was to "back out," keeping my face always towards Her Majesty, and the illustrious lord kindly gave me a specimen of that sort of backward locomotion. How far I profited by his instruction and example will presently appear.

We were conducted through a long corridor to a broad flight of marble steps, which led to the Queen's magnificent picture gallery, where Her Majesty and Prince Albert, the Duchess of Kent, the Duke of Wellington and others were awaiting our arrival. They were standing at the farther end of the room when the door was thrown open, and the General walked in, looking like a wax doll, gifted with the power of locomotion. Surprise and pleasure were depicted on the countenances of the royal circle at beholding this remarkable specimen of humanity so much smaller than they had evidently expected to find him.

The General advanced with a firm step, and, as he came within hailing distance, made a very graceful bow, and exclaimed: "Good evening, ladies and gentlemen!"

A burst of laughter followed this salutation. The Queen then took him by the hand, led him about the gallery, and asked him many questions, the answers to which kept the party in an uninterrupted strain of merriment. The General familiarly informed the Queen that her picture gallery was "first rate," and told her he should like to see the Prince of Wales. The Queen replied that the Prince had retired to rest, but that he should see him on some future occasion. The General then gave his songs, dances and imitations, and, after a conversation with Prince Albert and all present, which continued for more than an hour, we were permitted to depart.

Before describing the process and incidents of "backing out," I must acknowledge how sadly I broke through the counsel of the Lord in Waiting. While Prince Albert and others were engaged with the General, the Queen was gathering information from me in regard to his history, etc. Two or three questions were put and answered through the process indicated in my drill. It was a round about way of doing business, not at all to my liking, and I suppose the Lord in Waiting was seriously shocked, if not outraged, when I entered directly into conversation with Her Majesty. She, however, seemed not disposed to check my boldness, for she immediately spoke directly to me in obtaining the information which she sought. I felt entirely at ease in her presence, and could not avoid contrasting her sensible and amiable manners with the stiffness and formality of upstart gentility at home or abroad. The Queen was modestly attired in plain black, and wore no ornaments. Indeed, surrounded as she was by ladies arrayed in the highest style of magnificence, their dresses sparkling with diamonds, she was the last person whom a stranger would have pointed out in that circle as the Queen of England.

The Lord in Waiting was perhaps mollified towards me when he saw me following his illustrious example in "backing out" from the royal presence. He was accustomed to the process, and therefore was able to keep somewhat ahead (or rather aback) of me, but even *I* stepped rather fast for the General. We had a considerable distance to travel in that long gallery before reaching the door, and whenever the General found he was losing ground, he turned around and ran a few steps, then resumed the position of "backing out," then turned around and ran, and so continued to alternate his methods of getting to the door, until the gallery fairly rang with the merriment of the royal spectators. It was really one of the richest scenes I ever saw. Running, under the circumstances, was an offence sufficiently heinous to excite the indignation of the Queen's favorite poodle dog, and he vented his displeasure by barking so sharply as to startle the General from his propriety. He, however, recovered

immediately, and, with his little cane, commenced an attack on the poodle, and a funny fight ensued, which renewed and increased the merriment of the royal party.

This was near the door of exit. We had scarcely passed into the ante-room, when one of the Queen's attendants came to us with the expressed hope of Her Majesty that the General had sustained no damage; to which the Lord in Waiting playfully added, that in case of injury to so renowned a personage, he should fear a declaration of war by the United States!

On our second visit to the Queen, we were received in what is called the "Yellow Drawing-Room," a magnificent apartment, surpassing in splendor and gorgeousness anything of the kind I had ever seen. It was hung with drapery of rich yellow satin damask, the couches, sofas and chairs being covered with the same material. The vases, urns and ornaments were all of modern patterns, and the most exquisite workmanship. The room was panelled in gold, and the heavy cornices beautifully carved and gilt. The tables, pianos, etc., were mounted with gold inlaid with pearl of various hues, and of the most elegant designs.

We were ushered into this gorgeous drawing-room before the Queen and royal circle had left the dining-room, and, as they approached, the General bowed respectfully. The Queen smilingly took him by the hand, and said she hoped he was very well.

"General," continued the Queen, "this is the Prince of Wales."

"How are you, Prince," said the General, shaking him by the hand; and then standing beside the Prince, he remarked, "The Prince is taller than I am, but I *feel* as big as anybody," upon which he strutted up and down the room as proud as a peacock, amid shouts of laughter from all present.

The Queen then introduced the Princess Royal, and the General immediately led her to his elegant little sofa, which we took with us, and with much politeness sat himself down beside her. Then rising from his seat, he went through his various performances, and the Queen handed him an elegant and costly souvenir, which had been expressly made for him by her order, for which he told her he was very much obliged and he would keep it as long as he lived.

On our third visit to Buckingham Palace, Leopold, King of the Belgians, was also present. He was highly pleased and asked

a multitude of questions. Queen Victoria desired the General to sing a song, and asked him what song he preferred to sing.

"Yankee Doodle," was the prompt reply.

This answer was as unexpected to me as it was to the royal party. When the merriment it occasioned had somewhat subsided, the Queen good-humoredly remarked, "That is a very pretty song, General; sing it if you please." The General complied and soon afterward we retired.

The British public was now fairly excited. Not to have seen General Tom Thumb was decidedly unfashionable, and from March 20th to July 20th, the levees of the little General at Egyptian Hall were continually crowded. At the fashionable hour, sixty carriages of the nobility have been counted at one time standing in front of our exhibition rooms in Piccadilly. Pictures of the little General were published in all the pictorial papers of the time. Polkas and quadrilles were named after him and songs were sung in his praise.

The Queen Dowager Adelaide requested the General's attendance at Marlborough House one afternoon. He went in his court dress, consisting of a richly embroidered brown silk-velvet coat and shortbreeches, white satin vest with fancy colored embroidery, white silk stockings and pumps, wig, bagwig, cocked hat and a dress sword.

"Why, General," said the Queen Dowager, "I think you look very smart today."

"I guess I do," said the General.

A large party of the nobility was present. The old Duke of Cambridge offered the little General a pinch of snuff, which he declined. The General sang his songs, performed his dances and cracked his jokes, to the great amusement and delight of the distinguished circle of visitors.

"Dear little General," said the kind-hearted Queen, taking him upon her lap, "I see you have no watch. Will you permit me to present you with a watch and chain?"

"I would like them very much," replied the General, his eyes glistening.

"I will have them made expressly for you," responded the Queen Dowager, and at the same moment she called a friend and desired him to see that the proper order was executed. A few weeks thereafter we were called again to Marlborough House. A number of the children of the nobility were present as well as some of their parents. After passing a few compliments with the General, Queen Adelaide presented him with a beautiful little gold watch, placing the chain around his neck with her own hands.

This elegant little watch was not only duly heralded, but was also placed upon a pedestal in the hall of exhibition, together with the presents from Queen Victoria, and covered with a glass vase. To these were soon added an elegant gold snuff box mounted with turquoise, presented by his Grace the Duke of Devonshire, and many other costly gifts of the nobility and gentry. The Duke of Wellington called frequently to see the little General at his levees (that same Duke of Wellington who defeated the Emperor Napoleon in the battle of Waterloo). The first time he called the General was personating Napoleon, marching up and down the platform, and apparently taking snuff in deep meditation. He was dressed in the well-known uniform of the Emperor. I introduced him to the "Iron Duke," who inquired the subject of his meditations. "I was thinking of the loss of the Battle of Waterloo," was the little General's immediate reply. This display of wit was chronicled throughout the country.

Scarcely a nobleman in England failed to see General Tom Thumb at his own house, at the house of a friend, or at the public levees in Egyptian Hall. Our visit in London and tour through the provinces were enormously successful, and after a brilliant season in Great Britain, I made preparations to take the General to Paris. On the very day after my arrival, I received a special command to appear before King Louis Philippe at the Tuileries on the following Sunday evening.

At the appointed hour, the General and I, arrayed in the conventional court costume, were ushered into a grand saloon of the palace, where we were introduced to the King, the Queen, Princess Adelaide, the Duchess d'Orleans, her son, the Count de Paris, and a dozen or more distinguished persons. General Tom Thumb went through his various performances to the manifest pleasure of all who were present, and at the close the King presented to him a large emerald brooch set with diamonds.

King Louis Philippe was so condescending and courteous, that I felt quite at home in the royal presence, and ventured upon a bit of diplomacy. The Longchamps celebration was coming, a day now conspicuous for the display of court and fashionable equipages in the Champs Elysées and the Bois de Boulogne, and, as the King was familiarly conversing with me, I ventured to say that I had hurried over to Paris to take part in the Longchamps display, and I asked him if the General's carriage could not be permitted to appear in the avenue reserved for the court and the diplomatic corps, representing that the General's small but elegant establishment, with its tiny ponies and little coachman and footman, would be in danger of damage in the general throng unless the privilege I asked was accorded. The King

smilingly turned to one of the officers of his household, and, after conversing with him for a few moments, he said to me: "Call on the Prefect of Police tomorrow afternoon, and you will find a permit ready for you."

Longchamps day arrived, and among the many splendid equipages on the grand avenue, none attracted more attention than the superb little carriage with four ponies and liveried and powdered coachman and footman, belonging to the General. It stood out conspicuous in the line of carriages containing the

Ambassadors to the Court of France. Thousands upon thousands rent the air with cheers for "General Tom Pouce."

Thus, before I opened the exhibition, all Paris knew that General Tom Thumb was in the city. The season was more than a success; it was a triumph! The papers were profuse in their praises of the General and his performances. Statuettes of General Tom Pouce appeared in all the windows in plaster, marble, sugar, and chocolate.

We were commanded to appear twice more at the Tuileries, and we were also invited to the Palace on the King's birthday. One fourth and last visit to the royal family was by special invitation, at St. Cloud. We remained an hour, and, at parting, each of the royal party gave the General a splendid present.

After bidding them adieu, we retired to another portion of the palace to make a change of the General's costume and to partake of some refreshments which had been prepared for us. Half an hour afterward, as we were about leaving the palace, we went through a hall leading to the front door and, in doing so, passed the sitting-room in which the royal family was spending the evening. The door was open, and some of them, happening to espy the General, called out for him to come in and shake hands with them once more. We entered the apartment and found the ladies sitting around a table, each provided with two candles, and every one of them, including the Queen, was engaged in working at embroidery—a sight which I am sorry to say I believe is seldom seen in families of the aristocracy on either side of the water.

From France, we crossed the border into Belgium. Brussels is Paris in miniature and is, besides, one of the most charming cities I ever visited. The day after our arrival, by command, we visited King Leopold and the Queen at their palace. The King and Queen had already seen the General in London, but they wished to present him to their children and the distinguished persons whom we found assembled. After a most agreeable hour we came away, the General, as usual, receiving many fine presents.

The following day I opened the exhibition in a beautiful hall which, on that day and on every other day while we remained there, was crowded. On the second or third day, in the midst of the exhibition, I suddenly missed the case containing the valuable presents which the General had received from Kings, Queens, noblemen, and gentlemen, and instantly gave the alarm.

The police were notified, and I offered 2000-francs reward for the recovery of the property. A day or two afterward, a man went into a jeweler's shop and offered for sale, among other things, a gold snuffbox mounted with turquoises and presented by the Duke of Devonshire to the General. The jeweler, seeing the General's initials on the box, questioned the man, who became alarmed and ran out of the shop. An alarm was raised and the man was caught. He made a clean breast of it and, in the course of a few hours, the entire property was returned to the great delight of the General and myself. Wherever we exhibited afterward, the case of presents was always carefully watched.

From Belgium, we returned for a provincial tour through Great Britain. We traveled by post most of the time—that is, I had a suitable carriage made for our party and a van which conveyed the General's carriage, ponies, and such other property as we needed. We also used the railway lines freely, leaving our carriages at any station and taking them up again when we returned. I remember once making an extraordinary effort to reach a branch-line station where I meant to leave my teams and take the rail for Rugby. I had a timetable and knew at what time exactly I could hit the train, but unfortunately the axle to my carriage broke and I was an hour late in reaching the station. The train had long been gone, but I *must* be in Rugby where we had advertised a performance. I found the superintendent and told him, "I must instantly have an extra train to Rugby."

"Extra train," said he with surprise and a half-sneer, "why you can't have an extra train for less than sixty pounds."

"Is that all?" I asked. "Well, get up your train immediately. Here are your sixty pounds. What are sixty pounds to me."

The astonished superintendent bustled about and the train was soon ready. He was puzzled to know what distinguished person—he thought he must be dealing with some prince or at least a duke—was willing to give so much money to save a few hours' time, and he asked whom he had the honor of serving.

"General Tom Thumb!"

I had now spent three years with General Tom Thumb in Great Britain and on the Continent. The entire period had been a season of unbroken pleasure and profit. Thus closing a truly triumphant tour, we set sail for New York, arriving in February, 1847. The General immediately appeared in the American Museum, drawing such crowds as had never been seen before. We proceeded to Washington, visiting President Polk and lady at the White House, thence toured the East, the Southern States, and made a journey to Havana, where we were introduced to the Captain-General, and the Spanish nobility.

In 1849, I had projected a great traveling museum and menagerie. We chartered the ship *Regatta*, and despatched her to

Ceylon to procure elephants. The ship arrived in New York, in 1851, with ten elephants, and these, harnessed in pairs to a chariot paraded up Broadway. We added a caravan of wild animals and many museum curiosities and commenced operations under the patronage of General Tom Thumb who traveled nearly four years as one of the attractions of "Barnum's Great Asiatic Caravan, Museum, and Menagerie."

In 1861, I was visited at the Museum by a most remarkable dwarf, who was a sharp, intelligent little fellow perfectly formed with a deal of drollery and wit. His name, he told me, was George Washington Morrison Nutt. As soon as I engaged him, placards proclaimed the presence of Commodore Nutt at the Museum. I also procured for the Commodore a pair of Shetland ponies, miniature coachman and footman in livery, gold-mounted harness, and an elegant little carriage which, when closed, represented a gigantic English walnut. Commodore Nutt and the giantess, Anna Swan, show how extremes occasionally met at my Muesum. He was the smallest of men, and she was the tallest of women.

In 1862, I heard of an extraordinary dwarf named Lavinia Warren, a most intelligent and refined young lady, well-educated accomplished, and beautiful. I made an engagement with her and purchased for her a splendid wardrobe and costly jewels.

Tom Thumb called upon me quite unexpectedly one day while Lavinia was holding one of her levees. He had a short interview with her, after which he came directly to my private office and desired to see me alone.

"Mr. Barnum," he said, "that is the most charming little lady I ever saw and I believe she was created on purpose to be my wife."

His visits to the museum were now very frequent and it was noticeable that the Commodore who was on exhibition with her, though not exactly jealous, yet strutted around like a bantam rooster whenever the General approached Lavinia.

Tom Thumb finally returned to his home in Bridgeport, and privately begged that, on the following Saturday, I would take Lavinia up to my home in the same town. I could do no less than accede to his proposal; but, when the Commodore heard of the matter, he immediately pricked up his ears and said: "Mr. Barnum, I should like to go to Bridgeport to-morrow."

"What for?" I asked.

"I want to see my little ponies. I have not seen them for several months," he replied.

I whispered in his ear, "You little rogue, that is the pony you want to see," pointing to Lavinia.

The General met us at the depot in Bridgeport, on Saturday morning and drove us to my house in his own carriage—his coachman being tidily dressed with a broad velvet ribbon and silver buckle placed upon his hat expressly for the purpose. After resting half an hour at my home, he took Lavinia out to ride. He stopped a few moments at his mother's house, where she met his mother and saw the apartments which his father had built expressly for him and filled with the most gorgeous, tiny furniture—all corresponding to his own diminutive size.

Tom Thumb was with us for dinner and, as nine o'clock approached, I remarked that it was about time to retire, but somebody would have to sit up until eleven, in order to let in the Commodore, who was coming up on the late train. The General replied, "I will sit up with pleasure, if Miss Warren will remain also."

Lavinia carelessly replied that she was used to late hours and she would wait and see the Commodore, so the family retired.

Sometime afterward, Tom Thumb came rushing into my room. Closing the door he caught hold of my hand in a high state of excitement and whispered, "We are engaged, Mr. Barnum! We are engaged! We are engaged!" and he jumped up and down in the greatest glee.

When the Commodore heard the news he choked a little as if he was trying to swallow something. Then, turning to his heel, he said in a broken voice, "I hope you may be happy."

"Never mind, Commodore," I said to him, "Minnie Warren is a better match for you; she is a charming little creature and two years younger than you, while Lavinia is several years older."

A few weeks subsequently when time had reconciled the Commodore, he told me that Tom Thumb had asked him to stand as groomsman with Minnie as bridesmaid at the wedding.

The ceremony took place in Grace Church, New York, February 10, 1863. The church was filled by a highly-select audience of ladies and gentlemen. Among them were governors of several of the states, members of congress were present, also generals of the army, and many other prominent public men. After this, Mr. and Mrs. Tom Thumb started on a wedding tour taking in Washington on their way where they visited President Lincoln at the White House. They resumed their public career and have since traveled around the world, Commodore Nutt and Minnie Warren accompanying them. And the union of Mr. and Mrs. Tom Thumb has proved, in an eminent degree, a happy marriage.

Mr. Hampden's Shipwreck*

JOHN MASEFIELD

WHEN I was a youngster of about eighteen or nineteen I was stranded with a ship's company in a lonely reach of the Magellan Straits. The ship lost her way in a fog, and went on the rocks. We got ashore in a ship's boat, which was so dry from standing on deck that the seams all ran little rills. It is a gloomy part of the world. It is all rocky hills, frosted with snow, and torn with glaciers. Here and there was a colony of birds, all so tame that we could catch them. It was very bleak and grim, living there. We rigged up a shelter out of a sail. We used to sit and shiver, while the wind howled over us. I can tell you, the wind there takes the heart out of you. It comes up straight from the Pole, with a kind of yell which scares you. We had nothing much to drink, either, except melted snow. As for food, we had the birds, a few shellfish, and a few very precious sodden biscuits, which had been left long before in the boat's locker. They were in a horrible state, but they were great dainties to us. We had no other breadstuffs. Well, there we were, in a part of the world where no ships ever came. We didn't even know the name of the reach or bay into which we had come. There we were, so lost that sometimes a man would go out of the hut and wander up among the rocks, and stare at the loneliness, and then come back and cry. Lonely? You don't know what loneliness is till you look out of a hut in the morning and see an iron-grey sea sulky with frost, and the masts of your ship sticking out above the water. She had been a two-masted ship. Her name was the *Inesita*. There she was, deep in the sea, with the fish flipping in her hold, and those two iron fingers raised. We couldn't stand the sight of those two masts. In the end we rowed out with one of the boat flags, and a sailor named Jim Dane swarmed up and made it fast, so that she might cut a better figure.

There was a hill at the back of our camp. At least, when I

*From the *Book of Discoveries* by John Masefield.

call it a hill, I insult hills in general. It wasn't a hill. It was a rock from which all the earth had been washed away by the weather. It was an extinct volcano, about three thousand feet high. There was no grain of earth upon it, only shale and rock, which had been frozen and buffeted till they were rotten. It was like a black cake dusted with snow instead of sugar. We called it Mount Misery. We went up it soon after we landed, hoping that it would give us our bearings. We hoped to see the channel from it, or the smoke of some steamer in the channel, or at the worst the smoke of some Indian's fire. But nothing of the kind. One could see the Sound curving and winding, and hills like Mount Misery shutting out the view, and crags, and ghastly great boulders, and never a green thing. There were always clouds, too, not very far away. We would see them banked all round us, but always thicker to the south—always rather reddish, I remember. They gave one a feeling of being shut in. Yet, though they were never far off, they looked in a way like distant land—as though they were a kind of ghost-land into which the landscape turned. The worst of it was that they were always shutting down and blotting everything. They closed in twenty times a day. It would come on a thick whitish-yellow fog, wet as rain, and raw with cold—horrible!—and whenever this fog came down we couldn't see our hands in front of us.

Once we tried to get away, but first we had to caulk our boat with seaweeds, since she leaked like a sieve, and then we had to provision her. We killed a lot of stupid sea-birds. That was horrible, too, for I have always loved wild creatures. When we had provisioned the boat we had to water her.

Then the question came: Who should go in the boat? We couldn't all go. There were over thirty of us. The boat would only hold a dozen with any comfort, and I think everybody there was more than eager to be one of the first away. We spent a whole evening arguing about it, and then put it to the lot.

We drew matches out of the Captain's cap, and those who got the unburned matches were to go. The second mate and ten others were the lucky ones. They were the gladdest men in camp that night. They were in great spirits. They made sure that they had only to get out of the Sound to run into the main channel where the steamers pass two or three a day. To leave that camp was only a step to getting home. I thought of buying or, rather, of trying to buy the place of one of the lucky men, but then I felt that I ought not to do so. We were all equal there, and the Fates, or Providence, had chosen to give him this chance in preference to myself. I decided that I would bear what was coming to me like the rest, so I said nothing.

After the drawing of the lots, the second mate and the other officers argued and wrangled with the Captain about the course the boat should steer. They could not agree about it. They were not sure within twenty or thirty miles of where we could be. The Sound spread out its arms like a great grey octopus. It was heart-breaking to see it. How were we to know which arm led to the channel? We tramped along arm after arm over those miles of rotten rock. We would see the bends on ahead curving round the hills, and each bend led, as we thought, into the channel, but none did. You cannot think how cruel that branching water seemed. We called each arm by a bad name—Misery Harbour, Skunk's Delight, Disappointment, Old Footsore, etc. Well, it was decided at last. They gave the second mate a course, and when day dawned he sailed with his ten hands. We lined up on the beach, and gave them three cheers, and they gave us one cheer back; then we sang a sea-song called "Rolling Home," which sailors are very fond of singing. After that they cheered us again in the sea-fashion, with just one cheer. We saw them get smaller and smaller as they sailed away over the reach in the very light wind. It was a still morning, with a sort of hard grey rawness on it which made all things grim. The last face I saw of them was the second mate's face. He was standing up in the stern-sheets steering the boat with an oar.

We never saw them again. Whether they were drowned, or starved, or run down, or wrecked, we never heard. They just sailed away into—who knows what? Perhaps the natives killed them. Natives were a bad lot in those days. They cut off many poor fellows who were wrecked there. I like to think that they are all alive somewhere, though I'm afraid they were all dead before we left Port Misery. I like to think of them getting into the interior, to the settlements, to some good place or another, mining or ranching—not much chance of it, of course.

We were very melancholy after they had gone, but by the end of the day we had begun to be the brighter for it. We were so sure that they would get to the channel and be picked up by some ship. I remember that we talked among ourselves about the probable length of our stay there. The boat had sailed on Wednesday morning. She would be in the channel at latest, we thought, by Thursday noon, allowing for some delay in finding the way out of the pocket where we were. Thursday, at 3 p.m., as we reckoned, would be about the time for the Pacific liner from Punta Arenas to Chile. And if the Pacific liner passed the boat in a fog or snow-squall, as she well might, there would still be the Coronel Line's boat going the other way with the Chile mail. We reckoned to be out of the place aboard a good big liner within forty-eight hours. We waited three solid weeks there.

At first we were on tenterhooks all day long. Friday was a bad day. We were up betimes to make a smoke on Mount Misery as a sailing-mark. Most of us stayed on the Mount all the morning, going down in relays to get stuff for the fire—a kind of dry moss, a kind of peat. Towards noon we began to get anxious lest the boat or ship should come in a fog. I think all of us were a little afraid lest by some accident we should get left there. It was absurd, of course; but misfortune often makes people childish. Soldiers often cry when they have to fall back from a position. I've seen men cry because there was no water in the waterpan after a day in the desert. Cry? I've cried myself. One only grows up in certain things. A man's a great baby in most things till the end. Women have more sense.

By the early afternoon we had all left the mountain for the beach. We stood about on the beach looking out up and down the Sound, but there came no trace of any ship, not even the sound of a siren. We kept talking among ourselves, saying that it wouldn't be long before she came, or making excuses for her.

But in our hearts we thought all the time that the boat had come to grief somewhere. At dark we built up a good fire on the beach to guide them to us if they should come in the night. A good roaring blaze ought to show for five or six miles or more. We all worked hard gathering fuel for it. We still hoped, of course, for the steamer, but by dark we felt that something had gone wrong. None of us said so, only nobody protested when the Captain put us back to our allowance of salted bird. Ever since the boat sailed we had been eating as much as we pleased, thinking it foolish to stint ourselves when our misery was so nearly over. Now the Captain served out the allowance twice a day. It was roughly-salted sea-bird, tasting of fish, bad oil, and salt. Sometimes we had soup of it. What made it so horrible was its sameness.

Well, we picked watches that night. Some of us kept a bright look-out by the fire till Saturday morning. We saw nothing of any ship. Once we had a great start, thinking we heard the wash of a steamer's screws somewhere far off in the night; but it was nothing. Two of us said definitely that they had heard a ship; a third thought that it was like a ship's screws, but that it came from somewhere in the land. We listened with our ears close to the water's edge, but no sound came along the water. Our friends had been mistaken. Perhaps they heard a little fall of shale from one of the cliffs, or perhaps a big sea-bird or flock of birds swooped into the sea with that rushing scutter which sends them sliding twenty yards along the surface. Anyhow, it was not a ship's screws which they heard. That was not the only start we had during those watches. A shooting-star fell low down, and close to us (as it seemed)—so near to the water that those who saw it mistook it for a rocket. That was a lively alarm while it lasted, but it did not last long, of course. We very soon saw that we were wrong. After that nothing happened till daylight left us all free to turn in.

Saturday was not so hard to bear as Friday. The first disappointment and the keeping awake all night left us all a little dull and stupid. It was on Sunday that the real hardships began, for then we began to look at each other to see if anyone were going to be brave enough to say what all felt—that we were in a tight fix, without much chance of getting out of it. The Captain was a good man. He called us all up to him after mid-day dinner. He was an elderly man—sixty-five or so—married, with a family. He gave us a lecture on the situation which did him credit. He had lost his ship; he was hardly likely to get another at his age, even if we ever reached home; he had more home ties to brood over, and a harder future to look forward to, than any of us. But he was Captain still; he was responsible for us. I can't remember that he ever showed by any sign that the cards were against us. He told us that, although the boat had not returned, we were not to give up hope on that account. We were to pluck up heart, and cross no rivers till we came to the water. All the same, he said, we were beginning to be melancholy, which was a sign that we hadn't enough to do. He had been wrecked before, he said (on the coast of Hayti). I remember he made us all laugh here during his account of the wreck by telling us how the Captain of his ship had come ashore without his trousers. He said that on that occasion want of work had made the crew very melancholy, so that there had been a lot of trouble—"men drowning themselves, and silliness of that sort." He wasn't going to have anything of that kind while he commanded, so in future we were to work. The usual work of the camp—getting fuel, killing birds, keeping the fire going, and cooking—was not enough for us. He was going to set us a new task, which he meant us to do. We were to explore along the shore of the Sound till we found out where we were. We were to split up into parties of exploration. One-third of the company was to stay in camp in case the boat should return, one-third was to go up, the other third to go down, the Sound. Each exploring party was to travel for three days in its particular direction before returning to camp to report. So let us all cheer up, he said, and never mind the rotten rock, but step out boldly and find the channel. We cheered him when he finished. Afterwards we drew lots to decide which of us should go. I was drawn for the party of camp-keepers, unfortunately for myself. The Captain was quite right. Want of work does make shipwrecked people melancholy. Those black crags, and the water like steel, and the flurries of snow always blowing past—never enough to lie more than an inch, if as much, but always dusting down, fine and dry, on that dry cold wind from the Pole. Ugh! that was a horrid place! It lowered at one, and almost every day it started to blow a short, howling southwester which loosened your joints. A whirl of snow driving everywhere in a yell of wind which was like death. And nothing very much to do except to sit still to watch the snow coming.

Well, I learned then that I had wasted my time from my youth up. I had been to school—to an English school, that is—where I had learned to play cricket and to write very bad Latin verses; and now, for the first time, I was face to face with something which really taxed my mind, and showed me where I was empty. Some of my education had given me a tough, active body; another part of it had made me cheerful, and able to take whatever came without grumbling and troubling; but when I came to overhaul my mind for something to amuse me and take me out of myself, I found that I had very little—less even than the sailors. The sailors knew how to make things with their hands; they knew how to sing, how to dance step-dance, and how to endure. Whatever they knew, they knew thoroughly. It was a part of their lives. Whatever I knew, I knew partially. It was something I had read in a book. You must remember, too, that I was a landsman—the only landsman there.

Well, I had to find my amusement in myself, or go melancholy mad, like the men in the Captain's story. I set to work to imagine my home in the country. Whenever I was not working at my share of the camp duty, I was imagining the country which I knew as a boy. It was nothing very wonderful, of course. It was a little piece of Shropshire with a radius of about three miles, more or less. But it was England and home and whatever was dear to me. I went over every little bit of it time and time again. I tried to reconstruct that countryside in every detail, to make it real to my mind, so that I might, as it were, live there, or imagine myself living there, whenever the horror of Camp Misery became too great. I had lived in that little bit of the world for all the years of my boyhood; but when I came to build it up in my mind, so as to rest in it, there was so much that I had to write down as unexplored. There were so many blank spaces, fields which I had never entered, fields with shapes which I had forgotten, brooks with rapids and shallows which I could not place correctly, hedges into which I had never looked, animals and birds which I had shot at, perhaps, but never really known about. That seemed so strange to me, when I thought of it in Camp Misery—that I should have taken those creatures' lives without knowing what life meant to them, without ever having tried, or thought of trying, to know each strange little atom of life, so different, yet so alike. I made up my mind then and there that if I ever got back to England I would not waste my time again. I would look at the world with very different eyes; I would never forget, as I walked about, that the world is a continual miracle to be looked at earnestly, and remembered and read. Each little bit of the world is beautiful and interesting unspeakably. The more closely you look at a thing the more interesting it will become. All wisdom and all progress come from just that faculty of looking so closely at a thing that one can see its meaning as well as its appearance.

When I realized that I had wasted my time, and that I must never do so again, I realized, of course, that in a little while, perhaps, I should be away from that place forever. Yet it might be that in England or elsewhere, in a fit of loneliness, I might long for that place, and wish myself back there among the rocks. I said to myself that a man's moods are very fickle. Hate is only love turned upside down. I might love my memory of this place within the year. I felt that it was my duty to take an exact record of it, so that in after years I might never feel that I had failed to get out of it all that it had to teach me; so that I might not rebuke myself when a few comfortable weeks at home had turned my present hate of it the right way up. And when I came to examine it, and to look into it closely, there was an infinity of beauty and interest in it. I began to puzzle out to myself how it was that the plants and creatures had adapted themselves to the natural conditions there; why the moss was as it was; why the seaweeds were as they were; why some of the birds had longer bills than others; and what the rocks had been long ago, before the wear of the weather ground them down.

I went out on the next search expedition. We went about twenty miles along a never-ending wilderness of inlets. We didn't find anything, except on the last day one thing—a little cairn of stones with an iron bar sticking out of it, and a tin box tied to the end of the bar. Some of the sailors thought that it was the mark of some shipwrecked crew, but it was really a surveyor's mark. It had been there for years and years evidently.

We opened the tin box, hoping to find in it some writing from civilized people. You cannot imagine how eagerly we broke it open. We felt like people rifling the tomb of a King of Egypt. We did not know what secret might be hidden inside. There was nothing much inside except scraps of what had once been writing paper smeared with what had once been ink. All quite illegible. There wasn't even enough writing left to let us guess the date of the writer.

We couldn't make out from the position of the cairn whereabouts the open sea or the channel ought to be, for the very good reason that we were still on the wrong side of the Sound, and we found afterwards that the Sound reached on inland thirty miles from the farthest point reached by our explorers, so that it would have taken us a good five or six days' farther tramp to get round it to the side from which we could see the channel. We had been wrecked most miraculously in the most awkward possible place the ship could have chosen for us. If we had not been picked up by another miraculous chance we should have left our bones there.

The day before we went ashore, one of the hands had been set to put new life-lines on the life-buoys, of which, of course, we carried several. Well, as he worked upon them he managed to knock one overboard. He took a glance up and down to make sure that the loss had not been seen, and then went on with another life-buoy as though nothing had happened. As a matter of fact, a great deal had happened, for he had saved all our lives merely by knocking that life-buoy overboard. The life-buoy had the name of the ship *Inesita* painted upon it. While it floated it was a sort of advertisement of us. Anybody who found that life-

buoy would say to himself: "Yes; the ship *Inesita* has passed this way, and something strange has happened on board her."

The *Inesita* ran ashore the day after leaving Punta Arenas. She was bound through the Straits to a place called Coronel, in Southern Chile. While at Punta Arenas she lay at moorings near a ship called the *Chiloe*, which was about to sail through the Straits for the same place when we left the port. I suppose she started some twelve hours after us. Quite by chance her look-out man saw our lost life-buoy bobbing in the sea. He reported it to the officer of the watch, who had it fished on board. When the officer saw that it was the *Inesita's* buoy he reported it to his Captain, who came on deck at once. It had been very blind, squally weather. It was a very blind, bad part of the Straits. Anyone finding a buoy in such circumstances would have jumped to the conclusion that something was seriously wrong. A few minutes later it happened that the Captain of the *Chiloe* saw what he took to be drifting wreckage—a cask, and a half-submerged case or two, which looked like a water-logged boat or floating hen-coop. His mate said that it was undoubtedly ship's wreckage, and added that "it looked like the smash-up of the *Inesita*." They agreed that they had better poke about a bit to see what evidence they could find. They sent a man aloft to the crow's nest to look out for boats and survivors.

And then down came one of the bad Straits squalls, yelling like a battle. It gave them plenty to think of for the next hour or two. As for seeing through it, that was impossible. One couldn't see ten yards from the ship, nor hear a hail nor a signal. What with the wind blowing the snow into their eyes, and tearing off the tops of the waves to fling them, as they froze, over their heads, and the worst bit of the Straits ahead, those officers had no time to think of the *Inesita*. They had to use all their wits to make a head against the storm, and to win through to safety. When the squall blew over there was no trace of the *Inesita's* wreckage. What had been mistaken for it lay ten miles astern.

The *Chiloe* continued her passage westward. When she reached Coronel she reported the finding of the buoy, and the sighting of floating wreckage. People concluded that "something had happened," and that we were all drowned. Somebody cabled it to England, and a distorted line about it got into the papers.

But an elderly lady—a very good, energetic soul—a great friend of mine, saw the announcement, and wondered if I had got ashore by any chance. She felt quite sure at last that I was alive there somewhere, living on shell-fish, watching for a ship. She cabled to the British Consul at Punta Concha, but the Consul could tell her nothing further. In his opinion, the *Inesita* had sunk with all hands. We were "posted as missing," and my relatives ordered mourning.

But not my good friend. She was quite certain that I was alive somewhere. She came up to London, and set to work on the charts of the Straits to see where I might have got to. A nephew of hers, a young naval officer, helped her with them. They had the position of the *Chiloe* when she found the life-buoy, the set of the current, and that was all they had to go upon. Or not quite all. An eastward-bound steamer, which ought to have passed the *Inesita* near the mouth of the Straits, reported that she had seen no sign of us. So that put the scene of the disaster, if there had been one, between the mouth of the Straits and the place where the life-buoy had been found. They reckoned that the exact spot would be about twelve miles west of the spot where the life-buoy had been found. The young Lieutenant said: "Cable to the Consul at Punta Concha. Tell him to send out a tug to explore."

But for some reason this lady had taken a prejudice against the Consul. Something in his former cable made her suspect that he was not seriously interested. She had had some experience of the ways of Embassies years before, when anxious about a friend in Paris during the Revolution of the Commune. She decided that nothing could be done through them in this case. She was quite certain that I was alive there, with other men, and the feeling that she could do nothing to help me, and that if she did nothing it might soon be too late, was more than she could bear.

Early in the afternoon she made up her mind that she would come herself to find me. She obtained a sum of money, found out that she could catch the Liverpool mail-boat when it called at Plymouth for the London passengers, telegraphed for a berth in it, raked together what warm clothes she could buy in the time, and started directly. At Plymouth the agents of the steamship company told her that the ship was full. Those were the days of the great South American boom. The ships went out from England crammed with people bound for the Argentine, Chile, and Peru. This particular ship, the *Las Casas*, was full to the hatches; there was no room even in the steerage. Not a berth in her was to be had for money. However, my friend was not easily daunted. She hired a boat, piled her trunks aboard it, and put out to meet the steamer, which was due to arrive there to pick up the London passengers about midnight. It was blowing pretty fresh, with a good deal of rain, but she was determined not to put back till something had been done. A man would have gone to a hotel and smoked by the fire, but my friend was not

like that. She knew that the ship might only stay an hour there, or less even if there were no hitch. She was going to run no risks.

Presently the *Las Casas* came into the harbour. My friend ran alongside as she came to moorings, and they lowered a gang-way for her and picked her up. She said that she wanted to see the Captain. The Captain was very busy, but it is the custom of this world to let the people who really want a thing with their might and main have what they want, if only they keep on long enough. Presently the Captain came along fuming at being disturbed, and very well inclined to be rude. She told him her story there and then, and asked him to take her on board, offering to pay almost any sum for a berth if one could be found—any berth, a stewardess' berth or one of the officers' cabins. But no. It could not be done, he said. Money was no object; the ship was full. He wouldn't take another soul aboard if the Queen herself wanted a passage. That was his last word, he said, and he was a busy man. He couldn't stay there talking; he had a lot to see to. So away he went, grumbling about a lot of silly women wanting to throw the ship overboard. He left my friend aghast. She sat down, not knowing what to do, for the boats in those days only ran once a week, and a week's delay might be the end of every-thing. Presently her boatman came up grumbling to ask if she were soon coming to tell him what to do with her trunks. He wanted to be gone from there. He was wet through, and the boat was taking in water, for out there at the moorings it was bad weather for any boat. So she told him to bring her trunks on board and go. She gave him a sovereign for his trouble. I don't know why they let her trunks come on board, but in the confusion they did. The boatman left them and went. When he had gone she realized that she would be in a tight place if the Captain should prove a tartar. She saw herself being flung out of the ship into the tug which had brought the London passengers alongside.

Presently an elderly stewardess came past. My friend says

that the instant that stewardess appeared she knew that she had come to get her out of her trouble. She just rose up and said, "Stewardess, might I speak to you for a minute?" and the thing was done. I am ashamed to think how much it may have cost her, but she bribed that stewardess to give up her post. Within the next quarter of an hour they had settled everything. They had changed clothes. The stewardess had told her of her duties and shown her roughly the map of the ship, and where things could be found. She had introduced her to a friend (another stewardess), who promised to help in every way she could, and she had talked it over with the head-steward, to whom my friend promised five pounds if he would help her. The real stewardess had only just time to get off the ship before the bell rang for the tug to leave. Five minutes later the *Las Casas* was out of the harbour, butting into the heart of the channel, with spray coming over her in sheets. My friend was running about from passenger to passenger with tea and lemonade and ice. She had practically no rest until the ship left Lisbon. After the ship left Lisbon, when my friend knew that she could not be put ashore, she went boldly up and told the Captain what she had done. There was a scene. At first he vowed that he would make her work the full passage to Valparaiso. He was not going to be cheated out of a stewardess in that way. She was there on false pretenses; she was a stowaway; she was this, that, and the other. At last my friend told him frankly that, among other things, she was a lady, and meant to be treated as one. Soon after that the Captain was her very devoted humble servant, laughing with her at the trick she had played him, and admiring her pluck and energy. He offered her a berth, for one was now vacant, but she refused to take it. She would be a stewardess, she said, as far as the River Plate. At Monte Video, at the mouth of that river, she hoped to get some good Welsh or English woman to take her place.

She did her work very honestly. She was considered a model

stewardess. At Monte Video she engaged a substitute, but she would not leave her work till the day she left the ship at Punta Concha. Only thirty-four days after the *Inesita* went ashore, she landed alone in a little gloomy Magellan port, where a prison and a Consul's office stood out big above a lot of shanties and dock-side clutter.

Well, there is no need to make a longer tale of it. She learned that a sailing-cutter out in the harbour was bound through the Straits in two days. She went aboard her, and paid the Captain to sail two days earlier than he had planned. In three days from then the cutter discovered the inlet into which the *Inesita* had found her way.

When we really saw the cutter coming up to us, we were not much excited—not so much as I had thought we should be. We were a little dazed, perhaps, and in our hearts I think we were one and all a little sore about it. That place had been home to us for all those days. The first person whom I met when I got on board was my friend. She was leaning over the bulwarks, watching the boat come alongside. She was wearing a kind of sea-helmet or woolen face-protector which covers the cheeks. I didn't recognize her at first. When I did recognize her, I had no words with which to thank her. She discovered me, and I discovered what her friendship was worth.

A CHRISTMAS SONG AT SEA*

Alfred Noyes

In Devonshire, now, the Christmas chime
    Is carolling over the lea;
And the sexton shovels away the snow
    From the old church porch, maybe;
And the waits with their lanthorns and noses a-glow
    Come round for their Christmas fee;
But, as in old England it's Christmas-time,
    Why, so is it here at sea,
        My lads,
    Why, so is it here at sea!

*From *Collected Poems*. Used by permission of Frederick A. Stokes Company.

MEG MERRILIES

JOHN KEATS

Old Meg she was a gipsy,
And lived upon the moors;
Her bed it was the brown heath turf,
And her house was out of doors.

Her apples were swart blackberries,
Her currants pods o'broom;
Her wine was dew of the wild white rose,
Her book a churchyard tomb.

Her brothers were the craggy hills,
Her sisters larchen-trees;
Alone with her great family
She lived as she did please.

No breakfast had she many a morn,
No dinner many a noon,
And 'stead of supper she would stare
Full hard against the moon.

And with her fingers old and brown
She plaited mats of rushes,
And gave them to the cottagers
She met among the bushes.

Old Meg was brave as Margaret Queen,
And tall as Amazon;
An old red blanket cloak she wore,
A ship-hat had she on;
God rest her aged bones somewhere!
She died full long agone!

A child who lives among gypsies is pictured in music in *Mignon* by Ambroise Thomas, and *The Bohemian Girl* by Michael Balfe. "In the Gypsy's Life" and "Come with the Gypsy Bride" are from *The Bohemian Girl.*

Maggie Tulliver Goes to Live with the Gypsies*

GEORGE ELIOT

A WIDE plain where the broadening Floss hurries on between its green banks to the sea, and the loving tide rushing to meet it, checks its passage with an impetuous embrace. On this mighty tide the black ships are borne along to the town of St. Ogg's which shows its aged, fluted red roofs and the broad gables of its wharves between the low wooded hill and the river brink. Far away on each hand stretch the rich pastures and the patches of dark earth made ready for the seed. Just by the red-roofed town the tributary Ripple flows with a lively current into the Floss. And here is Dorlcote Mill with its trimly kept, comfortable dwelling house, as old as the elms and chestnuts that shelter it from the northern blast. The rush of the water and the booming of the mill bring a dreamy deafness which seems to heighten the peacefulness of the scene. And now there is the thunder of the huge covered wagon coming home with sacks of grain. That little girl who has stood so long on just the same spot at the edge of the stream is watching the unresting wheel sending out its diamond jets of water. And that queer white cur with the brown ear seems to be leaping and barking at the wheel; perhaps he is jealous because his playfellow is so rapt in its movement. It is time the little playfellow went in and there is a very bright fire to tempt her; the red light shines out from the left hand parlor where Mr. and Mrs. Tulliver are talking.

*Arranged from *The Mill on the Floss*, the story of George Eliot's life.

"It seems a bit of a pity," said Mr. Tulliver, "as the lad should take after the mother's side i'stead o' the little wench. The little un's twice as cute as Tom."

"Yes," said Mrs. Tulliver, "but her cuteness all runs to naughtiness. How to keep her in a clean pinafore two hours together passes my cunning. An' now you put me in mind," she continued, rising and going to the window, "I don't know where she is now, an' it's pretty nigh tea time. Ah, I thought so,—wanderin' up an' down by the water like a wild thing; she'll tumble in some day."

Mrs. Tulliver rapped the window sharply, beckoned, and shook her head,—a process which she repeated more than once before she returned to her chair.

"You talk o' cuteness, Mr. Tulliver," she observed as she sat down, "but I'm sure the child's half an idiot i' some things; for if I send her upstairs to fetch anything, she forgets what she's gone for, an' perhaps 'ull sit down on the floor i' the sunshine an' plait her hair an' sing to herself like a bedlam creatur' all the while I'm waiting for her down stairs. That niver run i' my family, thank God! no more nor a brown skin as makes her look like a mulatter!"

"Pooh, nonsense!" said Mr. Tulliver, "she's a straight, black-eyed wench as anybody need wish to see. I don't know i' what she's behind other folks' children; and she can read almost as well as the parson."

"But her hair won't curl all I can do with it, and she's so franzy about having it put i' paper, and I've such work as never was to make her stand and have it pinched with th' irons."

"Cut it off—cut it off short," said the father rashly.

"How can you talk so, Mr. Tulliver? She's too big a gell—gone nine and tall of her age—to have her hair cut short; an' there's her cousin Lucy's got a row o' curls round her head, an' not a hair out o' place. It seems hard as my sister Deane should have that pretty child. I'm sure Lucy takes more after me nor my own child does. Maggie, Maggie," continued the mother in a tone of half coaxing fretfulness, as Maggie entered the room, "where's the use o' my telling you to keep away from the water? You'll tumble in and be drownded some day an' then you'll be sorry you didn't do as mother told you."

Maggie's hair, as she threw off her bonnet, painfully confirmed her mother's accusation. Mrs. Tulliver, desiring her daughter to have a curled crop, "like other folks's children," had had it cut too short in front to be pushed behind the ears; and as it was usually straight an hour after it had been taken out of paper, Maggie was incessantly tossing her head to keep the dark heavy locks out of her gleaming black eyes,—an action which gave her very much the air of a small Shetland pony.

"Oh dear, oh dear, Maggie, what are you thinkin' of, to throw your bonnet down there? Take it upstairs, there's a good gell, an' let your hair be brushed, an' put your other pinafore on, an' change your shoes, do, for shame, an' come an' go on with your patchwork like a little lady."

"Oh, mother," said Maggie in a vehemently cross tone, "I don't *want* to do my patchwork."

"What! not your pretty patchwork, to make a counterpane for your Aunt Glegg?"

"It's foolish work," said Maggie with a toss of her mane—"tearing things to pieces to sew 'em together again. And I don't want to do anything for my Aunt Glegg. I don't like her."

And Maggie went out, dragging her bonnet by the string, while Mr. Tulliver laughed audibly.

"I wonder at you, as you'll laugh at her, Mr. Tulliver," said the mother with feeble fretfulness in her tone. "You encourage her i' naughtiness. An' her aunts will have it as it's me spoils her."

Few wives were more submissive than Mrs. Tulliver on all points unconnected with her family relations; but she had been a Miss Dodson, and the Dodsons were a very respectable family indeed,—as much looked up to as any in their own parish or the next to it. The Miss Dodsons had always been taught to hold up their heads very high. There were particular ways of doing everything in that family; particular ways of bleaching the linen, of making the cowslip wine, curing the hams and keeping the bottled gooseberries; so that no daughter of that house could be indifferent to the privilege of having been born a Dodson, rather than a Gibson or a Watson. And it is remarkable that while each individual Dodson was forever finding fault with every other individual Dodson, each was satisfied, not only with him or her self, but with the Dodsons as a whole. Mrs. Tulliver was a thorough Dodson. True, she had groaned a little in her youth under the yoke of her elder sisters, and still shed occasional tears at the disagreeable truths they never shrank from telling her, but she had no mind to let her husband or children fail in full respect to Aunt Glegg or any other member of the Dodson family. Now Tom was thought to be somewhat like the Dodsons,—he had light brown hair, cheeks of cream and roses, full lips and a nose and eyebrows expressing nothing in particular, a face as different as possible from poor Maggie's, which Nature seemed to have moulded and colored with the most decided intention. Mrs. Tulliver was thankful to have one child who took after her own family, at least in his features and complexion, but Tom was as far from appreciating his kin on his mother's side as Maggie herself, generally running away for the day with a large supply of the most portable food, when he received timely warning that his aunts and uncles were coming,—a moral symptom from which Aunt Glegg argued the gloomiest views for his future.

"My children are so awkward wi' their aunts and uncles,"

Mrs. Tulliver would sigh, "Maggie's ten times naughtier when they come than she is other days, and Tom doesn't like 'em. And there's Lucy Deane's such a good child,—you may set her on a stool and there she'll sit for an hour together, and never offer to get off."

It was Easter week and Mrs. Tulliver found it advisable to invite Sister Glegg, Sister Pullet and Sister Deane to dinner to consult with them on important matters. On Wednesday, the day before the aunts and uncles were coming, there were such various and suggestive scents as of plum cake in the oven and jellies in the hot state, mingled with the aroma of gravy, that it was impossible to feel altogether gloomy. Tom and Maggie made several inroads into the kitchen, and like other marauders, were induced to keep aloof for a time only by being allowed to carry away a sufficient load of booty.

"Tom," said Maggie, as they sat on the boughs of the elder-tree, eating their jam-puffs, "shall you run away tomorrow?"

"No," said Tom, slowly, when he had finished his puff, and was eyeing the third which was to be divided between them,—"no, I sha'n't."

"Why, Tom? Because Lucy's coming?"

"No," said Tom, opening his pocket-knife and holding it over the puff with his head on one side in an uncertain manner. (It was a difficult problem to divide that very irregular polygon into two equal parts.) "What do I care about Lucy? She's only a girl,—she can't play at bandy."

"Is it the tipsy cake, then?" said Maggie, while she leaned forward towards Tom with her eye fixed on the hovering knife.

"No, you silly, that'll be good the day after. It's the pudden. I know what the pudden's to be,—apricot roll-up. O my buttons!"

With this interjection the knife descended on the puff and it was in two, but the result was not satisfactory to Tom, for he still eyed the halves doubtfully—one was decidedly better than the other.

"Shut your eyes, Maggie."

"What for?"

"You never mind what for. Shut 'em when I tell you."

Maggie obeyed.

"Now which'll you have, Maggie,—right or left?"

"I'll have that with the jam run out," said Maggie, keeping her eyes shut to please Tom.

"Why, you don't like that, you silly. You may have it if it comes to you fair, but I sha'n't give it you without. Right or left,—choose now. Ha!" said Tom in a tone of exasperation as Maggie peeped. "You keep your eyes shut else you sha'n't have any."

Maggie would gladly have given up the best piece to Tom, but her power of sacrifice did not extend so far as to go without any, so she shut her eyes quite close till Tom told her to "say which," and then she said, "Left hand."

"You've got it," said Tom in rather a bitter tone.

"What! the bit with the jam run out?"

"No; here take it," said Tom, firmly handing the best piece to Maggie.

"Oh, please, Tom, have it; I don't mind—I like the other; please take this."

"No, I sha'n't," said Tom crossly, beginning on his own piece.

Maggie, thinking it was no use to contend further, began too, and ate up her half puff with considerable relish as well as rapidity. But Tom had finished first and had to look on while Maggie ate her last morsel or two, feeling in himself a capacity for more.

"Oh, you greedy thing," said Tom when she had finished the last morsel. He was conscious of having acted very fairly, and thought she ought to have considered this and made up to him for it. He would have refused a bit of hers beforehand, but one has naturally a different point of view before and after one's own share of puff is swallowed.

Maggie turned quite pale. She loved Tom with all the strength of her warm, impetuous nature and could not bear to have him think ill of her. "Oh, Tom," she cried, "why didn't you ask me?"

"I wasn't going to ask you, you greedy. You might have thought of it without, when I gave you the best bit."

"But I wanted you to have it; you know I did," said Maggie.

"Yes, but I wasn't going to do what wasn't fair. If I go halves, I'll go 'em fair; only I wouldn't be a greedy."

With this cutting remark, Tom jumped down from his bough and walked off, throwing a stone with a "hoigh!" as a friendly attention to Yap, the dog, who had also been looking on while the eatables vanished with an agitation of the ears and feelings which could hardly have been without bitterness. Yet the excellent dog accepted Tom's attention with as much alacrity as if he had been treated quite generously

But Maggie sat still on her bough and gave herself up to the keen sense of unmerited reproach. She would have given the world not to have eaten all her puff, and to have saved some of it for Tom. She would have gone without it many times over, sooner than Tom should call her greedy and be cross with her. And he had said he wouldn't have it, and she ate it without thinking; how could she help it? The tears flowed so plentifully that Maggie saw nothing around her for the next ten minutes; but by that time resentment began to give way to the desire for reconciliation, and she jumped from her bough to look for Tom.

The next day the Dodsons arrived, one and all, at Dorlcote Mill. Aunt and Uncle Glegg came first, Aunt Glegg in her severe bonnet and slate colored gown with a mouldy odor about it, suggestive of a damp clothes chest. Then came Aunt and Uncle Pullet in a one-horse chaise. Mr. Pullet was a small man with a high nose, small twinkling eyes and thin lips, who bore about the same relation to his tall good-looking wife with her balloon sleeves, abundant mantle, and large be-feathered and be-ribboned bonnet as a small fishing smack bears to a brig with all its sails spread. Lastly, appeared Mr. and Mrs. Deane with little Lucy, and Mrs. Tulliver had to look on with a silent pang while Lucy's blond curls were adjusted. Maggie always looked twice as dark as usual when she was by the side of Lucy.

She did today when she and Tom came in from the garden with their father and their Uncle Glegg. Maggie had thrown her bonnet off very carelessly, and, coming in with her hair rough as well as out of curl, rushed at once to Lucy who was standing by her mother's knee. Certainly the contrast between the cousins was conspicuous; it was like the contrast between a rough, dark, overgrown puppy and a white kitten. Lucy put up the neatest little rosebud mouth to be kissed; everything about her was neat—her little round neck with the row of coral beads; her little straight nose, not at all snubby; her little clear eyebrows rather darker than her curls to match her hazel eyes which looked up with shy pleasure at Maggie, taller by the head, though scarcely more than a year older. Maggie always looked at Lucy with delight. She was fond of fancying a world where the people never grew any larger than children of their own age, and she made the queen of it just like Lucy, with a little crown on her head and a little sceptre in her hand—only the queen was Maggie herself in Lucy's form.

"Oh, Lucy," she burst out, after kissing her, "you'll stay with Tom and me, won't you? Oh, kiss her, Tom."

Tom, too, had come up to Lucy, but he was not going to kiss her—no; he came up to her with Maggie because it seemed easier on the whole than saying, "How do you do?" to all those aunts and uncles. He stood looking at nothing in particular with the blushing, awkward air and semi-smile which are common to shy boys when in company.

"Heyday!" said Aunt Glegg with loud emphasis. "Do little boys and gells come into a room without taking notice o'their uncles and aunts? That wasn't the way when I was a little gell."

"Go and speak to your aunts and uncles, my dears," said Mrs. Tulliver looking anxious. She wanted to whisper a command to Maggie to go and have her hair brushed.

"Well, and how do you do? And I hope you're good children, are you?" said Aunt Glegg, in the same loud emphatic way as she shook their hands, hurting them with her large rings, and kissing their cheeks much against their desire. "Look up, Tom, look up. Boys as go to boarding schools should hold their heads up. Look at me now." Tom declined the pleasure apparently, for he tried to draw his hand away. "Put your hair behind your ears, Maggie, and keep your frock on your shoulder."

Aunt Glegg always spoke to them in this loud, emphatic way, as if she considered them deaf, or perhaps rather idiotic; it was a means, she thought, of making them feel that they were accountable creatures, and might be a salutary check on naughty tendencies. Bessy's children were so spoiled—they'd need have somebody to make them feel their duty.

"Well, my dear," said Aunt Pullet in a compassionate voice, "you grow wonderful fast. I think the gell has too much hair. I'd have it thinned and cut shorter if I was you; it isn't good for her health. It's that as makes her skin so brown, I shouldn't wonder. Don't you think so, sister Deane?"

"I can't say, I'm sure, sister," said Mrs. Deane, shutting her lips close again and looking at Maggie with a critical eye.

"No, no!" said Mr. Tulliver, "the child's healthy enough; there's nothing ails her. But it 'ud be as well if Bessy 'ud have her hair cut so as it 'ud lie smooth."

A dreadful resolve was gathering in Maggie's breast, but it was arrested by the desire to know from her Aunt Deane whether she would leave Lucy behind. Aunt Deane would hardly ever let Lucy come to see them. After various reasons for refusal, Mrs. Deane appealed to Lucy herself.

"You wouldn't like to stay without mother, should you, Lucy?"

"Yes, please, mother," said Lucy timidly, blushing very pink all over her little neck.

"Well done, Lucy! Let her stay, Mrs. Deane, let her stay," said Mr. Deane.

"Maggie," said Mrs. Tulliver, beckoning Maggie to her and whispering in her ear as soon as this point of Lucy's staying was settled, "go and get your hair brushed, do, for shame. I told you not to come in without going to Martha first; you know I did."

"Tom, come out with me," whispered Maggie, pulling his sleeve as she pushed him, and Tom followed willingly enough.

"Come upstairs with me, Tom," she whispered when they were outside the door. "There's something I want to do before dinner."

"There's no time to play at anything before dinner," said Tom.

"Oh, yes, there is time for this; come, Tom."

Tom followed Maggie upstairs and saw her go at once to

a drawer, from which she took out a large pair of scissors.

"What are they for, Maggie?" said Tom, feeling his curiosity awakened.

Maggie answered by seizing her front locks and cutting them straight across the middle of her forehead.

"Oh, my buttons! Maggie, you'll catch it!" exclaimed Tom; "you'd better not cut any more off."

Snip! went the great scissors again while Tom was speaking, and he couldn't help feeling it was rather good fun; Maggie would look so queer.

"Here, Tom, cut it behind for me," said Maggie, excited by her own daring and anxious to finish the deed.

"You'll catch it, you know," said Tom, nodding his head in an admonitory manner, and hesitating a little as he took the scissors.

"Never mind, make haste!" said Maggie, giving a little stamp with her foot. Her cheeks were quite flushed.

The black locks were so thick, nothing could be more tempting to a lad who had already tasted the forbidden pleasure of cutting the pony's mane. One delicious grinding snip and then another and another, and the hinder-locks fell heavily on the floor, and Maggie stood cropped in a jagged uneven manner but with a sense of clearness and freedom as if she had emerged from a wood into the open plain.

"Oh, Maggie," said Tom, jumping around her, and slapping his knees as he laughed, "oh, my buttons! what a queer thing you look! Look at yourself in the glass; you look like the idiot we throw out nut-shells to at school."

Maggie felt an unexpected pang. She had thought beforehand chiefly of her own deliverance from her teasing hair and teasing remarks about it, and something also of the triumph she would have over her mother and her aunts by this very de-

cided course of action. But now, when Tom began to laugh at her and say she was like the idiot, the affair had quite a new aspect. She looked in the glass and still Tom laughed and clapped his hands, and Maggie's flushed cheeks began to pale and her lips to tremble a little.

"Oh, Maggie, you'll have to go down to dinner directly," said Tom. "Oh, my!"

"Don't laugh at me, Tom," said Maggie with an outburst of angry tears, stamping and giving him a push.

"Now, then, spitfire," said Tom. "What did you cut it off for then? I shall go down. I can smell the dinner going in."

He hurried down stairs and left poor Maggie to bitterness. She could see clearly enough now the thing was done, that it was very foolish, and that she should have to hear and think more about her hair than ever, for Maggie rushed to her deeds with passionate impulse and then saw their consequences afterward. Tom never did the same sort of foolish things as Maggie, having a wonderful instinctive discernment beforehand of what would turn to his advantage or disadvantage; and so it happened that, though he was much more wilful and inflexible than Maggie, his mother hardly ever called him naughty. But if Tom ever did make a mistake of that sort he stood by it. If he broke the lash of his father's gig-whip by lashing the gate, he couldn't help it,—the whip shouldn't have got caught in the hinge. He was convinced, not that the whipping of gates by all boys was a justifiable act, but that he, Tom Tulliver, was justifiable in whipping that particular gate, whereas Maggie was always being sorry and wishing she had done something different.

As she stood crying before the glass, Maggie felt it impossible that she should go down to dinner and endure the severe eyes and severe words of her aunts; and if she had only let her hair alone, she could have sat with Tom and Lucy, and had the apricot pudding and the custard! What could she do but sob?

"Maggie," said Tom, peeping into the room ten minutes after, "why don't you come and have your dinner? There's lots o' goodies and mother says you're to come. What are you crying for, you little spooney?"

Oh, it was dreadful! Tom was so hard and unconcerned; if *he* had been crying on the floor, Maggie would have cried too. And there was the dinner, so nice; and she was *so* hungry. It was very bitter. But Tom was not altogether hard; he was not inclined to cry and did not feel that Maggie's grief spoiled his prospect of the sweets; but he went and put his head near her and said in a lower comforting tone,—

"Won't you come then, Maggie? Shall I bring you a bit o' pudding when I've had mine, and a custard and things?"

"Ye-e-es," said Maggie, beginning to feel life a little more tolerable.

"Very well," said Tom, going away. But he turned again at the door and said, "But you'd better come, you know. There's the dessert,—nuts, you know, and cowslip wine."

Maggie's tears had ceased and she looked reflective as Tom left her. His good-nature had taken off the keenest edge of her suffering and nuts with cowslip wine began to assert their legitimate influence.

Slowly she rose from her scattered locks, and slowly she made her way downstairs. Then she stood with one shoulder against the frame of the dining-parlor door, peeping in when it was ajar. She saw Tom and Lucy with an empty chair between them, and there were the custards on a side table. It was too much! She slipped in and went toward the empty chair. But, she had no sooner sat down, than she repented and wished herself back again.

Mrs. Tulliver gave a little scream as she saw her and dropped the large gravy spoon into the dish with the most serious results to the tablecloth. Mrs. Tulliver's scream made all eyes turn toward the same point as her own, and Maggie's cheeks and ears began to burn, while Uncle Glegg, a kind-looking, white-haired old gentleman, said: "Heyday! what little gell's this? Why, I don't know her. Is it some little gell you've picked up in the road?"

"Why, she's gone and cut her hair, herself," laughed Mr. Tulliver in an undertone to Mr. Deane.

"Why, little miss, you've made yourself look very funny," said Uncle Pullet and, perhaps he never in his life made a remark which was felt to be more cutting.

"Fie, for shame!" said Aunt Glegg in her loudest, severest tone of reproof. "Little gells as cut their own hair should be whipped and fed on bread and water."

"Ay, ay," said Uncle Glegg, meaning to give a playful turn to this denunciation, "she must be sent to jail I think, and they'll cut the rest of her hair off there and make it all even."

"She's more like a gypsy nor ever," said Aunt Pullet.

"She's a naughty child, as'll break her mother's heart," said Mrs. Tulliver with tears in her eyes.

Maggie seemed to be listening to a chorus of reproach and derision. Her first flush came from anger, which gave her a momentary power of defiance. "Oh, my! Maggie, I told you you'd catch it," whispered Tom. He meant to be friendly, but Maggie felt convinced that Tom was rejoicing in her shame. Her feeble power of defiance left her in an instant, her heart swelled and,

getting up from her chair, she ran to her father, hid her face on his shoulder, and burst into loud sobbing.

"Come, come, my wench," said her father soothingly putting his arm around her, "never mind! You was i' the right to cut it off if it plagued you. Give over crying, father'll take your part!"

Delicious words of tenderness!

"How your husband does spoil that child, Bessy!" said Mrs. Glegg in a loud "aside" to Mrs. Tulliver. "It'll be the ruin of her if you don't take care."

Mrs. Tulliver's sorrows seemed to have reached the point where she could feel no more. She took no notice of her sister's remark, but carved the pudding in mute resignation.

With the dessert, there came entire deliverance for Maggie, for the children were told they might have their nuts and wine in the summer house, since the day was so mild. They scampered out among the budding bushes of the graden with the alacrity of small animals getting from under a burning glass.

That night all the uncles and aunts departed, leaving Lucy Deane behind, but the next day, Mrs. Tulliver was to take the children to Sister Pullet's, at Garum Firs, for tea. The day began ill with Maggie. The prospect of the afternoon visit at Garum Firs, where she would hear Uncle Pullet's musical box, had been marred as early as eleven o'clock by the advent of the hair-dresser from St. Ogg's, who had spoken in the severest terms of the condition in which he had found her hair, holding up one jagged lock after another and saying, "See here! Tut, tut, tut!" in a tone of mingled disgust and pity, which, to Maggie's imagination, was equal to the strongest expression of public opinion.

Already at twelve o'clock Mrs. Tulliver had on her visiting costume, with a protective covering of brown holland. Maggie was frowning and twisting that she might, if possible, shrink away from the prickliest of tuckers, while her mother was remonstrating, "Don't, Maggie, my dear! Don't make yourself so ugly!"

As for Lucy, she was just as pretty and neat as she had been yesterday. She looked with wondering pity at Maggie, pouting and writhing under the exasperating tucker. Maggie would certainly have torn it off, if she had not been checked by the memory of her recent humiliation about her hair. As it was, she confined herself to fretting and twisting and behaving peevishly about the card houses which they were allowed to build till dinner as a suitable amusement for boys and girls in their best clothes. Tom could build perfect pyramids of houses, but Maggie's would never bear the laying on of the roof. It was always so with the things that Maggie made, and Tom had concluded that no girls could ever make anything. But it happened that Lucy proved wonderfully clever at building; she handled the cards so lightly and moved so gently that Tom condescended to admire her houses. Maggie, too, would have admired Lucy's houses if Tom had not inconsiderately laughed when her houses fell and told her she was "a stupid."

"Don't laugh at me, Tom!" she burst out angrily. "I'm not a stupid. I know a great many things you don't."

"Oh, I daresay, Miss Spitfire! I'd never be such a cross thing as you, making faces like that. Lucy doesn't do so. I like Lucy better than you. I wish Lucy was *my* sister."

"Then it is very wicked and cruel of you to wish so," said Maggie, starting up hurriedly from her place on the floor and upsetting Tom's wonderful pagoda. She really did not mean to do it, but Tom turned white with anger. He would have struck her, only he knew it was cowardly to strike a girl and Tom Tulliver was quite determined he would never do anything cowardly.

Maggie stood in dismay and terror while Tom got up from the floor and walked away, pale, from the ruin of his pagoda.

"Oh, Tom," said Maggie at last, going half-way toward him, "I didn't mean to knock it down, indeed, indeed I didn't."

Tom took no notice of her, but took, instead, two or three hard peas out of his pocket and shot them against the window.

Thus the morning had been made heavy to Maggie, and Tom's persistent coldness to her all through their walk to Garum Firs spoiled the fresh air and sunshine for her. Still, the sight of the peacock spreading his tail on the stackyard wall, just as they

reached Garum Firs, was enough to divert the mind for a time from grievances. And this was only the beginning of beautiful sights at Garum Firs. All the farmyard life was wonderful there —bantams, speckled and top-knotted; Friesland hens with their feathers all turned the wrong way; Guinea fowls that flew and screaned and dropped their pretty, spotted feathers; pouter pigeons and a tame magpie; nay, a goat and wonderful brindled dog, half-mastiff, half-bulldog, as large as a lion. Then there were white railings and white gates all about and glittering weathercocks of various design and gardenwalks paved with pebbles in beautiful patterns—nothing was quite common at Garum Firs.

Uncle Pullet had seen the expected party approaching from the window and made haste to unbar and unchain the front door, kept always in this fortified condition from fear of tramps, who might be supposed to know of the glass case of stuffed birds in the hall and to contemplate rushing in and carrying it away on their heads. Aunt Pullet, too, appeared at the doorway and, as soon as her sister was within hearing, said: "Stop the children, for God's sake, Bessy! Don't let 'em come up the doorstep! Sally's bringing the old mat and the duster to rub their shoes!"

When the ceremony of shoe-wiping was over, Aunt Pullet conducted Mrs. Tulliver and the girls in solemn procession upstairs along the bright and slippery corridor into the darkened best room where the outer light, entering feebly, showed what looked like the ghosts of furniture in white shrouds. Meanwhile, Tom was seated below in irksome constraint on the edge of a sofa directly opposite his Uncle Pullet.

"Well, young sir, what do you learn at school?" was a standing question with Uncle Pullet. Whereupon Tom always looked sheepish, rubbed his hands across his face, and answered, "I don't know."

The appearance of the little girls suggested to Uncle Pullet that he offer them certain small sweet cakes, of which he kept a stock under lock and key for his own private eating on wet days; but the children had no sooner got the tempting delicacy between their fingers, than Aunt Pullet desired them to abstain from eating it till the tea-tray and the plates came, since with these crisp cakes they would make the floor "all over" crumbs. Lucy didn't mind that much, for the cake was so pretty she thought it rather a pity to eat it; but Tom, watching his opportunity while the elders were talking, hastily stowed his in his mouth at two bites and chewed it furtively. As for Maggie, becoming fascinated as usual by a colored print on the wall, she presently let fall her cake, and in an unlucky movement crushed it beneath her foot,—a source of so much agitation to Aunt Pullet and disgrace to Maggie that she began to despair of hearing the musical snuff box today, till it occurred to her that Lucy was in high favor enough to venture on asking for a tune. So she whispered to Lucy; and Lucy, who always did what she was desired to do, went up quietly to her uncle's knee, and blushing all over her neck while she fingered her necklace, said, "Will you please play us a tune, Uncle?"

When the fairy tune began, Maggie quite forgot that she had a load on her mind, that Tom was angry with her; and by the time that "Hush, ye pretty warbling choir," had been played, her face wore that bright look of happiness while she sat immovable with her hands clasped, which sometimes comforted her mother with the sense that Maggie could look pretty now and then, in spite of her brown skin. But when the magic music ceased, she jumped up, and running towards Tom, put her arm around his neck and said, "Oh Tom, isn't it pretty?"

Now this caress was to Tom quite uncalled for. Moreover he had his glass of cowslip wine in his hand, and Maggie jerked him so that she made him spill half of it.

"Look there now!" he cried angrily.

"Why don't you sit still!" her mother said peevishly.

"Little gells mustn't come to see me if they act like that," said Aunt Pullet.

"Why you're too rough, little miss," said Uncle Pullet.

Poor Maggie sat down again with the music all chased out of her soul and the seven small demons all in again. Mrs. Tulliver, foreseeing nothing but misbehavior while the children remained indoors, took an early opportunity of suggesting that, now they were rested after their walk, they might go and play out of doors; and Aunt Pullet gave permission, only bidding them not to go off the paved walks in the garden, and if they wanted to see the poultry fed, to view them from a distance on the horse-block, a restriction which had been imposed upon the children ever since Tom had been found guilty of running after the peacock, with a vague idea that fright would make one of its feathers drop off.

All the disagreeable recollections of the morning were thick upon Maggie when Tom, whose displeasure towards her had been considerably refreshed by her foolish trick of causing him to upset his cowslip wine, said, "Here, Lucy, you come along with me," and walked off to the area where the toads were, as if there were no Maggie in existence. Seeing this, Maggie lingered at a distance, looking like a small Medusa with her snakes cropped. Lucy was naturally pleased that cousin Tom was so good to her, and it was very amusing to see him tickling a fat toad with a piece of string when the toad was safe down the area with an iron grating over him. Still Lucy wished Maggie to enjoy the spectacle also, especially as she would doubtless find a name for the toad, and say what had been his past history; for Lucy had a delighted semi-belief in Maggie's stories about the live things they came upon by accident—how Mrs. Earwig had a wash at home, and one of her children had fallen into the hot copper for which reason she was running so fast to fetch the doctor. Tom had a profound contempt for this nonsense of Maggie's, smashing the earwig at once as a superflous yet easy means of proving the entire unreality of such a story; but Lucy, for the life of her, could not help fancying there was something in it, and at all events thought it was very pretty make-believe. So now the desire to know the history of a very portly toad, added to her habitual affectionateness, made her run back to Maggie and say, "Oh, there is such a big funny toad, Maggie! Do come and see!"

Maggie said nothing but turned away from her with a deeper frown. As long as Tom seemed to prefer Lucy to her, Lucy made part of his unkindness.

Tickling a fat toad is an amusement that it is possible to exhaust and Tom by and by began to look around for some other mode of passing the time. But in so prim a garden where they were not to go off the paved walks, there was not a great choice of sport. The only great pleasure such a restriction suggested was the pleasure of breaking it, and Tom began to mediate a visit to the pond, about a field's length from the garden.

"I say, Lucy, he began, as he coiled up his string again, "what do you think I mean to do?"

"What, Tom?" said Lucy with curiosity.

"I mean to go to the pond and look at the pike. You may go with me if you like," said the young sultan.

"Oh, Tom, *dare* you?" said Lucy. "Aunt said we mustn't go out of the garden."

"Nobody 'ull see us," said Tom. "Besides I don't care if they do—I'll run off home."

"But I couldn't run," said Lucy who had never before been exposed to such severe temptation.

"Oh, never mind; they won't be cross with *you*," said Tom. "You say I took you."

Tom walked along and Lucy trotted by his side, timidly enjoying the rare treat of doing something naughty,—excited also by the mention of that celebrity the pike, about which she was quite uncertain whether it was a fish or a fowl. Maggie saw them leaving the garden and could not resist the impulse to follow. That Tom and Lucy should do or see anything of which she was ignorant would have been an intolerable idea to Maggie. So she kept a few yards behind them unobserved by Tom, who was presently absorbed in watching for the pike,—a highly interesting monster. The pike, like other celebrities, did not show when he was watched for, but Tom caught sight of something which attracted him to another spot on the brink of the pond.

"Here, Lucy," he said in a loud whisper, "come here! Take care! Keep on the grass! Don't step where the cows have been!" he added, pointing to a peninsula of dry grass with trodden mud on each side of it.

Lucy came carefully as she was bidden, and bent down to look at what seemed a golden arrow-head darting through the water. It was a water-snake, Tom told her; and Lucy at last could see the serpentine wave of its body. Maggie had drawn nearer and nearer; she *must* see it too, though it was bitter to her like everything else since Tom did not care about her seeing it. At last she was close by Lucy; and Tom, who had been aware of her approach, but would not notice it till he was obliged, turned round and said,—

"Now get away, Maggie; there's no room for you on the grass here. Nobody asked *you* to come."

There were passions at war in Maggie at that moment to have made a tragedy, but the utmost she could do, with a fierce thrust of her small brown arm, was to push poor little pink-and-white Lucy into the cow-trodden mud.

Then Tom could not restrain himself, and gave Maggie two smart slaps on the arm as he ran to pick up Lucy who lay crying helplessly. Maggie retreated to the roots of a tree a few yards off and looked on impenitently. Usually her repentance came quickly after one rash deed, but now Tom and Lucy had made her so miserable, she was glad to spoil their happiness,—glad to make everybody uncomfortable. Why should she be sorry? Tom was slow to forgive her, however sorry she might have been.

"I shall tell mother, you know, Miss Mag," said Tom loudly and emphatically as soon as Lucy was up and ready to walk away, crying piteously. It was not Tom's practice to "tell," but here justice clearly demanded that Maggie should be visited with the utmost punishment.

"Sally," said Tom when they reached the kitchen door, and Sally looked at them in speechless amaze, with a piece of bread-and-butter in her mouth and a toasting-fork in her hand,—"Sally, tell mother it was Maggie pushed Lucy into the mud."

"But Lors ha' massy, how did you get near such mud as that?" said Sally making a wry face.

Tom's imagination had not been rapid enough to include this question among the foreseen consequences, but it was no sooner put than he foresaw that Maggie would not be considered the only culprit in the case. He walked quietly away from the kitchen door, leaving Sally to the pleasure of guessing. Sally lost no time in presenting Lucy at the parlor door.

"Goodness gracious!" Aunt Pullet exclaimed, "Keep her at the door, Sally! Don't bring her off the oil-cloth, whatever you do!"

"Why she's tumbled into some nasty mud," said Mrs. Tulliver, going up to Lucy to examine into the amount of damage.

"If you please, 'um, it was Miss Maggie as pushed her in," said

Sally. "Master Tom's been and said so, and they must h'a been to the pond for it's only there they could ha' got into such dirt."

Mrs. Tulliver was mute, feeling herself a truly wretched mother, while Mrs. Pullet began to give elaborate directions to Sally how to gaurd the premises from serious injury in the course of removing the dirt. Mrs. Tulliver went out to speak to her naughty children supposing them to be close at hand; but it was not until after some search that she found Tom leaning with a rather hardened, careless air against the white paling of the poultry yard.

"Tom, you naughty boy, where's your sister?" said Mrs. Tulliver in a distressed voice.

"I don't know," said Tom; his eagerness for justice on Maggie had diminished since he had seen that it could hardly be brought about with the injustice of some blame on his own conduct.

"Why, where did you leave her?" said his mother, looking round.

"Sitting under the tree against the pond," said Tom.

"Then go and fetch her in this minute, you naughty boy."

You may conceive the terrified search for Maggie and the difficulty of convincing her mother that she was not in the pond—tea deferred, and the poultry alarmed by the unusual running to and fro, till Mr. Pullet, confused and overwhelmed, reached down a key to unlock the goose-pen as a likely place for Maggie to lie concealed in. Tom started the idea that Maggie was gone home and the suggestion was seized as a comfort by his mother.

"Sister, for goodness' sake let 'em put the horse in the carriage and take me home. Lucy can't walk in her dirty clothes," she said, looking at that innocent victim who was wrapped up in a shawl and sitting with naked feet on the sofa. Aunt Pullet was quite willing to take the shortest means of restoring her premises to order and quiet, and it was not long before Mrs. Tulliver was in the chaise, looking anxiously at the most distant point before her.

Maggie's intentions, as usual, were on a larger scale than Tom had imagined. The resolution that gathered in her mind, after

Tom and Lucy had walked away, was not so simple as that of going home. No, she would run away and go to the gypsies, and Tom should never see her anymore. That was by no means a new idea to Maggie. She had been so often told she was like a gypsy and "half-wild," that, when she was miserable, it seemed to her the only way of escaping blame would be to live in a little brown tent on the commons. The gypsies, she considered, would gladly receive her and pay her much respect on account of her superior knowledge. She had once mentioned her views on this point to Tom, and suggested that he should stain his face brown and they should run away together. But Tom rejected the scheme with contempt, observing that gypsies were thieves and hardly got anything to eat and had nothing to drive but a donkey. Today, however, Maggie thought her misery had reached a pitch at which gypsydom was her only refuge. She rose from her seat on the roots of the tree with the sense that this was a great crisis in her life. She would run straight away till she came to Dunlow Common, where there would certainly be gypsies, and cruel Tom and the rest of her relations should never see her anymore. She thought of her father as she ran along, but she reconciled herself to the idea of parting with him by determining that she would secretly send him a letter by a small gypsy, who would run away without telling where she was and just let him know that she was well and happy and always loved him very much.

Maggie soon got out of breath with running. She presently passed through the gate into the lane, not knowing where it would lead her. But she was soon aware, not without trembling, that there were two men coming along the lane in front of her. The formidable strangers were two shabby-looking men with flushed faces, one of them carrying a bundle on a stick over his shoulder. The man with a bundle stopped, and in a half-whining, half-coaxing tone asked her if she had a copper to give a poor man. Maggie had a sixpence in her pocket—her Uncle Glegg's present—

which she immediately gave this poor man with a polite smile, hoping he would feel kindly toward her as a generous person.

"That's the only money I've got," she said apologetically.

"Thank you, little miss," said the man in a less respectful and grateful tone than Maggie anticipated, and she even observed that he smiled and winked at his companion. She walked on hurriedly but was aware that the two men were standing still, probably to look after her, and she presently heard them laughing loudly. It was clear that she was not likely to make a favorable impression on passengers, and she thought she would turn into the fields again. She turned through the first gate that was not locked, and felt a delightful sense of privacy in creeping along by the hedge rows. Sometimes she had to climb over high gates, but she was getting out of reach very fast and should probably soon come within sight of Dunlow Common. She hoped so, for she was getting rather tired and hungry; and, until she reached the gypsies, there was no definite prospect of bread and butter. At last, however, the green fields came to an end, and Maggie found herself looking through the bars of a gate into a lane where she saw a donkey with a log tied to his foot feeding on the grassy margin. She crept through the bars of the gate and walked on with new spirit, though not without haunting images of Apollyon, and a highwayman with a pistol, and a blinking dwarf in yellow with a mouth from ear to ear, and other miscellaneous dangers.

It was not without a leaping of the heart that she caught sight of a small pair of bare legs sticking up, feet uppermost, by the side of a hillock. They seemed something hideously preternatural—a diabolical kind of fungus—for she was too much agitated at the first glance to see the ragged clothes and the dark, shaggy head attached to them. It was a boy asleep, and Maggie trotted along faster lest she should wake him. It did not occur to her that he was one of her friends, the gypsies, who, in all probability, would have very genial manners. But the fact was so, for, at the next bend in

the lane, Maggie actually saw the little, semi-circular tent, with the blue smoke rising before it, which was to be her refuge. She even saw a tall, female figure by the column of smoke, doubtless the gypsy-mother who provided the tea and other groceries. It was astonishing to her that she did not feel more delighted. She went on, however, and it was plain she had attracted attention for the tall woman, who proved to be a young woman with a baby on her arm, walked slowly to meet her. Maggie looked up in the new face rather tremblingly and was reassured by the thought that her Aunt Pullet and the rest were right when they called her a gypsy; for this face, with the bright dark eyes and the long hair, was really something like what she used to see in the glass before she cut off her hair.

"My little lady, where are you going to?" the gypsy said in a tone of coaxing deference. It was delightful and just what Maggie expected. The gypsies saw at once that she was a little lady and were prepared to treat her accordingly.

"Not any farther," said Maggie, feeling as if she were saying what she had rehearsed in a dream. "I'm come to stay with *you*."

"That's pretty; come then! Why, what a nice little lady you are to be sure!" said the gypsy, taking her by the hand. Maggie thought her very agreeable, but wished she had not been so dirty.

There was quite a group round the fire. An old gypsy woman was seated on the ground nursing her knees and occasionally poking a skewer into the kettle that sent forth an odorous steam. Two small, shock-headed children were lying prone and resting on their elbows and a placid donkey was bending his head over a tall girl, who, lying on her back, was scratching his nose and indulging him with a bit of excellent stolen hay. The slanting sunlight fell kindly upon them and the scene was very pretty, Maggie thought, only she hoped they would soon set out the teacups. Everything would be quite charming when she had taught the gypsies to use a wash basin and to feel an interest in books.

It was a little confusing, though, that the young woman began to speak to the old one in a language which Maggie did not understand, while the tall girl, who was feeding the donkey, sat up and stared at her without offering any salutation. At last the old woman said, "What! my pretty lady, are you come to stay with us? Sit ye down and tell us where you come from."

It was just like a story. Maggie liked to be called pretty lady and treated in this way. She said, "I'm come from home because I'm unhappy and I mean to be a gypsy. I'll live with you if you like, and I can teach you a great many things."

"Such a clever little lady," said the woman with the baby, sitting down by Maggie and allowing baby to crawl, "and such a pretty bonnet and frock," she added, taking off Maggie's bonnet and looking at it while she made an observation to the old woman in the unknown language. The tall girl snatched the bonnet and put it on her own head hind-foremost with a grin; but Maggie was determined not to show any weakness on this subject.

"I don't want to wear a bonnet," she said. "I'd rather wear a red handkerchief, like yours (looking at her friend by her side).

"Oh, what a nice little lady! And rich, I'm sure," said the old woman. "Didn't you live in a beautiful house at home?"

"Yes, my home is pretty, and I'm very fond of the river where we go fishing, but I'm often very unhappy. I should have liked to bring my books with me, but I came away in a hurry you know. But I can tell you almost everything there is in my books, I've read them so many times, and that will amuse you. And I can tell you something about geography, too, that's about the world we live in. Did you ever hear about Columbus?"

Maggie's eyes had begun to sparkle and her cheeks to flush. She was really beginning to instruct the gypsies and gaining great influence over them. The gypsies themselves were not without amazement at this talk, though their attention was divided by the contents of Maggie's pocket, which the friend at her right hand had, by this time, emptied without attracting her notice.

"Is that where you live, my little lady?" said the old woman at the mention of Columbus.

"Oh, no!" said Maggie with some pity, "Columbus was a very wonderful man who found out half the world, and they put

chains on him and treated him very badly, you know, but perhaps it's rather too long to tell before tea—*I want my tea so.*"

The last words burst from Maggie in spite of herself, with a sudden drop from patronising instruction to simple peevishness.

"Why, she's hungry, poor little lady," said the younger woman. "Give her some o' the cold victual. You've been walking a good way, I'll be bound, my dear. Where's your home?"

"It's Dorlcote Mill, a good way off," said Maggie. "My father is Mr. Tulliver, but we mustn't let him know where I am, else he'll fetch me home again. Where does the queen of the gypsies live?"

"What! do you want to go to her, my little lady?" said the younger woman. The tall girl meanwhile was constantly staring at Maggie and grinning. Her manners certainly were not agreeable.

"No," said Maggie, "I'm only thinking that if she isn't a very good queen, you might choose another. If I was a queen, I'd be a very good queen and kind to everybody."

"Here's a bit o' nice victual, then," said the old woman, handing to Maggie a lump of dry bread, which she had taken from a bag of scraps, and a piece of cold bacon.

"Thank you," said Maggie, looking at the food without taking it, "but will you give me some bread-and-butter and tea instead? I don't like bacon."

"We've got no tea nor butter," said the old woman, with something like a scowl, as if she were getting tired of coaxing.

"Oh, a little bread and treacle would do," said Maggie.

"We ha'n't got no treacle," said the old woman crossly, whereupon there followed a sharp dialogue between the two women in their unknown tongue and one of the small sphinxes snatched at the bread-and-bacon and began to eat it. At this moment the tall girl who had gone a few yards off, came back, and said something which produced a strong effect. The old woman, seeming to forget Maggie's hunger, poked the skewer into the pot with new vigor, and the younger crept under the tent, and reached out some platters and spoons. Maggie trembled a little and was afraid the tears would come into her eyes. Meanwhile the tall girl gave a shrill cry and presently came running up the boy whom Maggie had passed as he was sleeping,—a rough urchin about the age of Tom. He stared at Maggie and there ensued much incomprehensible chattering. She felt very lonely, and was quite sure she should begin to cry before long; the gypsies didn't seem to mind her at all, and she felt quite weak among them. But the springing tears were checked by a new terror when two men came up whose approach had been the cause of the sudden excitement. The elder of the two carried a bag which he flung down, addressing the women in a loud and scolding tone, which they answered by a shower of treble sauciness; while a huge cur ran barking up to Maggie, and threw her into a tremor that only found a new cause in the curses with which the younger man called the dog off, and gave him a rap with a great stick he held in his hand.

Maggie felt that it would be impossible she should ever be queen of these people, or ever communicate to them amusing and useful knowledge. Both of the men now seemed to be inquiring about Maggie for they looked at her. At last the younger woman said in her previous deferential, coaxing tone,—

"This nice little lady's come to live with us; aren't you glad?"

"Ay, very glad," said the younger man, who was looking at Maggie's silver thimble and other small matters that had been taken from her pocket. He returned them all except the thimble to the younger woman with some observation, and she immediately restored them to Maggie's pocket, while the men seated themselves and began to attack the contents of the kettle—a stew of meat and potatoes,—which had been taken off the fire and turned out into a yellow platter. Maggie began to think that Tom must be right about the gypsies; they certainly must be thieves unless the man meant to return her thimble by-and-by. She would willingly have given it to him, for she was not at all attached to her thimble; but the feeling that she was among thieves prevented her from feeling any revival of deference and attention towards her; all thieves except Robin Hood were wicked people. The women saw she was frightened.

"We've got nothing nice for a lady to eat," said the old woman in her coaxing tone. "And she's so hungry, sweet little lady."

"Here, my dear, try if you can eat a bit o' this," said the younger woman, handing some of the stew on a brown dish with an iron spoon to Maggie, who, remembering that the old woman had seemed angry with her for not liking the bread-and-bacon, dared not refuse the stew, though fear had chased away her appetite. If her father would but come by in the gig and pick her up! Or even if Jack the Giantkiller, or Mr. Greatheart, or St. George who slew the dragon would happen to pass that way! But Maggie thought with a sinking heart that these heroes were never seen in the neighborhood of St. Ogg's; nothing very wonderful ever came there.

Maggie's ideas about gypsies had undergone a rapid modification in the last five minutes. From having considered them very respectable companions, amenable to instruction, she had begun to think that they meant perhaps to kill her as soon as it was dark, and cut up her body for gradual cooking; the suspicion crossed her that the fierce-eyed old man was perhaps the devil, who might drop that disguise at any moment and turn into the grinning blacksmith, or else a fiery-eyed monster with dragon's wings. It was no use trying to eat the stew and yet the thing she most dreaded was to offend the gypsies by betraying her extremely unfavorable opinion of them.

"What! you don't like the smell of it, my dear?" said the young woman, observing that Maggie did not even take a spoonful of the stew. "Try a bit, come?"

"No, thank you," said Maggie, summoning all her force for a desperate effort, and trying to smile in a friendly way. "I haven't time, I think; it seems getting darker. I think I must go home now, and come again another day, and then I can bring you a basket with some jam tarts and things."

Maggie rose from her seat, devoutly hoping her hint about the tarts would tempt Apollyon to let her go, but her hope sank when the old gypsy woman said, "Stop a bit, little lady; we'll take you home all safe, when we've done supper. You shall ride home like a lady."

Maggie sat down again with little faith in this promise, though she presently saw the tall girl putting a bridle on the donkey, and throwing a couple of bags on his back.

"Now then, little missis," said the younger man, rising and leading the donkey forward, "tell us where you live."

"Dorlcote Mill is my home," said Maggie eagerly. "My father is Mr. Tulliver. He lives there."

"What! a big mill a little way this side o' St. Ogg's?"

"Yes," said Maggie. "Is it far off? I think I should like to walk there, if you please."

"No, no, it'll be getting dark; we must make haste. And the donkey'll carry you as nice as can be; you'll see."

He lifted Maggie as he spoke, and set her on the donkey. She felt relieved that it was not the old man who seemed to be going with her, but she had only a trembling hope that she was really going home.

"Here's your pretty bonnet," said the younger woman, putting that recently despised but now welcome article of costume on Maggie's head; "and you'll say we've been very good to you, won't you, and what a nice little lady we said you was."

"Oh, yes, thank you," said Maggie, "I'm very much obliged to you, but I wish you'd go with me, too." She thought anything was better than going with one of the dreadful men alone.

"Ah, you're fondest o' me, aren't you?" said the woman. "But I can't go. You'll go too fast for me."

It now appeared that the man also was to be seated on the donkey holding Maggie before him, and she was as incapable of remonstrating against this arrangement as the donkey himself, though no nightmare had ever seemed to her more horrible. When the woman had patted her on the back and said, "Good-bye," the donkey at a strong hint from the man's stick set off at a rapid walk along the lane towards the point Maggie had come from an hour ago, while the tall girl and the rough urchin, also furnished with sticks, obligingly escorted them for the first hundred yards with much screaming and thwacking.

Not Leonore, in that preternatural midnight excursion with her phantom lover, was more terrified than poor Maggie in this entirely natural ride on a short-paced donkey, with a gypsy behind her who considered he was earning half-a-crown. The red light of the setting sun seemed to have a portentous meaning, with which the alarming bray of the second donkey with the log on its foot must surely have some connection. Two low, thatched cottages—the only houses they passed in this lane—seemed to add to its dreariness; they had no windows to speak of, and the doors were closed; it was probable that they were inhabited by witches, and it was a relief to find that the donkey did not stop there.

At last—oh, sight of joy!—this lane, the longest in the world, was coming to an end, was opening on a broad highroad where there was actually a coach passing! And there was a finger-post at the corner,—she had surely seen that finger-post before,—"To St. Ogg's 2 miles." The gypsy really meant to take her home then; he was probably a good man after all, and might have been rather hurt at the thought that she didn't like coming with him alone. This idea became stronger as she felt more and more certain that she knew the road quite well, and she was considering how she might open a conversation with the injured gypsy, and not only gratify his feelings but efface the impression of her cowardice, when, as they reached a cross-road, Maggie caught sight of someone coming on a white-faced horse.

"Oh, stop, stop!" she cried out. "There's my father! Oh, father, father!"

The sudden joy was almost painful, and before her father reached her, she was sobbing. Great was Mr. Tulliver's wonder,

for he had made a round from Basset, and had not yet been home.

"Why, what's the meaning o' this?" he said, checking his horse, while Maggie slipped from the donkey and ran to his stirrup.

"The little miss lost herself, I reckon," said the gypsy. "She'd come to our tent at the far end o' Dunlow Lane, and I was bring ing her where she said her home was. It's a good way to come arter being on the tramp all day."

"Oh, yes, father, he's been very good to bring me home," said Maggie,—"a very kind, good man!"

"Here, then, my man," said Mr. Tulliver, taking out five shillings. "It's the best day's work you ever did. I couldn't afford to lose the little wench; here lift her up before me."

"Why Maggie, how's this how's this?" he said as they rode along, while she laid her head against her father and sobbed. "How come you to be rambling about and lose yourself?"

"Oh, father," sobbed Maggie, "I ran away because I was so unhappy; Tom was so angry with me. I couldn't bear it."

"Pooh, pooh," said Mr. Tulliver, soothingly, "you mustn't think o' running away from father. What 'ud father do without his little wench?"

"Oh, no, I never will again, father—never."

Mr. Tulliver spoke his mind very strongly when he reached home that evening; and the effect was seen in the remarkable fact that Maggie never heard one reproach from her mother, or one taunt from Tom, about this foolish business of her running away to the gypsies. Maggie was rather awe-stricken by this unusual treatment, and sometimes thought that her conduct had been too wicked to be alluded to.

11 12 13 14 15 - 88 87 86 85 84